D1095592

HENRY L. DOHERTY SERIES

REVISED EDITION

◆

◆

◆

Elements of
Petroleum Reservoirs

NORMAN J. CLARK

Copyright © 1960 by the Society of Petroleum
Engineers of The American Institute of Mining, Metallurgical, & Petroleum Engineers, Inc.

Copyright © 1969 by the American Institute of
Mining, Metallurgical, & Petroleum Engineers,
Inc.

6200 North Central Expressway
Dallas, Texas 75206

All Rights Reserved.
This book, or parts there-
of, cannot be reproduced
without written consent
of the publisher.

Printed in the United States of America

Norman J. Clark
(1915-1977)
In Memoriam

During his 32-year career in the petroleum engineering field as manager, consultant, and researcher, Norman J. Clark directed technical advances in field development and performed reservoir studies on hundreds of fields in North and South America, the Mid East, and Europe. He received a BS degree in mathematics and physics from Southwest Texas State Teachers College in 1937. Clark became a corrosion engineer with Barnsdall Refining Co. and Barnsdall Pipe Line Co. in Texas during 1937-39. In 1941, he received a BS degree in petroleum engineering from the U. of Oklahoma and joined Humble Oil & Refining Co. Clark worked in equipment research and development with the U.S. Navy Bureau of Ordnance during WW II. At Humble, he supervised reservoir-engineering training of engineers and managers in Houston and developed a formation evaluation program. In 1955, he began organizing an engineering and consulting department for Core Laboratories, Inc., in Dallas. As assistant department manager, Clark supervised reservoir engineering and geological consulting work, including the first U.S. condensing gas-drive pilot project to be expanded into field-wide operation. In 1958, he formed Norman J. Clark Engineering in Dallas, a petroleum consulting firm he headed until retirement in 1969. His consulting specialties were reservoir-engineering studies and economics, and property appraisal. Long an active member of the Society of Petroleum Engineers, Clark served as chairman of its General Editorial Committee in 1958 and as Distinguished Lecturer during 1967-68. *Elements of Petroleum Reservoirs* was first published in the Society's Henry L. Doherty Series in 1960 and revised in 1969. Clark also wrote a series of definitive technical articles on reservoir fluids and their calculation that appeared in the *Journal of Petroleum Technology* in early 1962. He was also a frequent contributor to other petroleum-industry publications. He was registered in Texas as a professional engineer, and a member of the Petroleum Engineers Club of Dallas and the Engineers Club of Dallas. Clark died Feb. 11, 1977, in Dallas at the age of 61.

Foreword

Elements of Petroleum Reservoirs is a book for investors, managers, supervisors and engineers—in fact, anyone who might be more than casually interested in how petroleum is, and can be, produced.

A vast amount of technology has been developed and is available to produce our hydrocarbon resources. Here it is explained so that those who have use for it can develop an increased understanding to lead to more efficient and more profitable operations.

Elements of the science of oil recovery are treated in sequence, starting with basic geology and the formation of the various types of reservoirs and reservoir rocks. The reader then becomes acquainted with all of the various physical factors that have a bearing on hydrocarbon recovery—how fluids flow through the reservoir rock, and how this flow can be altered to produce greater recovery and profits.

Engineering processes one ordinarily considers extremely complicated are treated in a lucid manner and with the aid of excellent illustrations.

The material presented by Mr. Clark ranges from tried and proved procedures to new and challenging concepts. A greater comprehension of the problems of oil and gas recovery, and their solutions, awaits the reader.

BURTON ATKINSON

◆

◆

◆

Preface

For many decades after 1859—the recognized beginning of our domestic oil industry—history reveals that finding and producing oil was conducted on a basis of feast or famine. The technologist was absent from the scene until about 1914 when the petroleum geologist started well-sitting as we know it today. This actually broke a barrier that was jealously guarded by the driller at that time and gave oil finding the beginning of its guidance through technology. Then some two decades later in the middle 1930's, a new science in petroleum production engineering began to evolve.

This relatively new science, now referred to as "reservoir engineering", became available on a practical and widespread basis only after World War II, in the late 1940's. It deals with occurrence and movement of fluids in reservoirs and their recovery, and its application embodies a thorough study and evaluation of all factors affecting recovery of oil and gas to determine the most efficient and profitable method of production commensurate with economic trends.

Although the ultimate total amount of oil to be produced from a given property has always been of great concern to the producer, he did not recognize during the first 50 to 75 years of our industry that only a small percentage of the oil was produced by primary means from the reservoirs discovered. During the last decade when good reservoir engineering has been widely available, however, great strides have been made toward increasing the recovery percentage of oil discovered.

The Society of Petroleum Engineers of AIME has reported

that a major oil company estimated total oil found in place in all reservoirs in the United States to be 230 billion barrels as of Jan. 1, 1956. Estimated ultimate oil recovery expected from all these known reservoirs on that date was 84.1 billion barrels, or 35 per cent of the original oil found. An alarming amount of oil is being left in the ground, either because we have not known how to recover it economically or because we have not applied the improved recovery techniques known for a number of years to be highly successful.

Oil and gas are becoming more costly to find and many operators are competing intensively for every barrel found. Every operator should, therefore, recognize that the economic future of his company is based on only a small portion of oil originally occupying the reservoir. Sound operations based on proper engineering and planning usually result in great financial gains through increased oil recoveries.

The first approach toward increasing recovery usually is the adoption of operating procedures that will more effectively use native energy in the reservoir to produce the oil. Still further increases in efficiency can often be brought about by altering the primary recovery mechanism of the reservoir through fluid injections—such as gas injection, pressure maintenance or waterflood operations. These operations have all proved highly successful when properly applied. Proper application, of course, requires proper engineering and careful planning for each individual field and reservoir involved.

A total of 402 unitized fluid injection projects in 15 states were reported to the Interstate Oil Compact Commission in 1957 as being representative of pressure maintenance practices in the United States. These fields contained over 26 billion barrels of oil initially in place; 42.8 per cent, or 11.2 billion barrels, ultimate recovery is expected from these fields by pressure maintenance or secondary recovery operations. Only 6.7 billion barrels of oil, or about 25.7 per cent, ultimate recovery was expected by primary operations. Thus, 4.5 billion barrels were added to the nation's reserve by these projects. Although this additional oil represents a large quantity of added reserve, it accomplishes only a small portion of the over-all job ahead because a major part of the original oil will still be left in the ground even after these conventional pressure maintenance projects are abandoned.

Therefore, the industry is working toward developing new and better oil recovery processes and improving applications of both the presently known and the new and better engineering techniques as they are developed in the future.

Just what the subject of reservoir engineering embraces and to what extent it enters into production problems have been subjects of widespread speculation by management and staff men alike. The science is still in its infancy and involves new technical approaches. This book is the result of an effort to describe and illustrate the complex science of reservoir behavior and control in as simple and straight-forward a manner as practical. By this means it is hoped that greater knowledge of the scope of reservoir behavior may be visualized by beginning engineers, management supervisors and other interested people and, further, that the relationship of reservoir engineering to production operation will be better understood and the benefits of its application realized on a wider scale.

The author is especially appreciative for the approval and financial backing given this book by the Henry L. Doherty Memorial Fund, and is honored to have the book published as part of the Henry L. Doherty Series.

The author is grateful to his many colleagues who through the years have assisted in the development of ideas presented in this book. Particular thanks are given to T. G. Roberts and J. D. Lindner for their assistance in the preparation of the final manuscript; to Joe B. Alford, of the Society of Petroleum Engineers of AIME, for encouragement and administrative work in readying the manuscript for publication; and to R. W. Taylor, D. L. Riley and Ann Gibson, of the Society of Petroleum Engineers, whose editorial assistance was invaluable. Appreciation is expressed to P. D. White and Jon T. Moss, of Tejas Petroleum Engineers, for writing Chapter 14, "Combustion Drive".

NORMAN J. CLARK

April, 1960
Dallas, Texas

Contents

x

◆

◆

◆

CHAPTER 1

How Petroleum
Was Formed and How
It Gathered Into Reservoirs

The Earth at Dawn

The history of the origin and accumulation of petroleum is written in geologic signs found in the formations of the earth that were laid down throughout the earth's existence. The story of petroleum or "rock oil" transcends the earth's geologic time; therefore, the entire story includes all chapters of the earth's existence.

Scientists and astronomers do not agree on how the earth was formed. Some propose that the earth, as well as other planets of our sun, was formed as a result of a collision of another sun with our sun in which a great splash of molten rock was thrown into space. They claim that this great mass of rock splattered into many small masses that separated and became planets, planetoids, comets and other bodies in space. The earth thus was formed as one of these planets that revolves about our sun. Other scientists propose that a great nebula of cosmic dust swirled around a vortex; particles forming the nebula condensed by attractive gravitation and formed the sun. Outer rings of particles coalesced and turned into the individual planets of our universe.

Although the question of how the earth was formed may always be the subject of speculation, the question of when the earth was formed is thought to be fairly well established. Radioactive materials decay in a known period of time, and the age of rocks containing these materials can be determined by calculating current degrees of the decay process.

Whether the earth started as a gaseous mass or as molten rock, it passed through a molten stage and cooled sufficiently at the surface to form solid rock masses. According to scientists, these first rock masses formed some four or five billion years ago.

During a period of further cooling, the earth shrank. The crust buckled and warped like the skin of a drying prune. Gaseous materials and steam spewed forth from the earth, and after further evolution and cooling, atmosphere and oceans were formed. Continents took shape from the solidified rock, and annual rhythmic climatic changes commenced.

Mountains Are Formed

The oceans covering the major part of the earth's surface are well known for their currents. Although several factors cause these currents, earth motion is recognized as a major reason that they continue. Just as this motion propels the great water basins, it also is believed to cause currents to take place in the molten rock of the earth's interior.

Although much of the warping and other crustal movements of the earth were at one time caused by the earth shrinkage through cooling, it appears that during most of the earth's geologic past crustal movements were caused by plastic flow of inner molten rock. These movements caused great mountain ranges to rise and great seas to form (Fig. 1). Age after geologic age saw mountains changing positions to the extent that sea floors became mountains and mountains submerged into the seas.

While mountains protruded and fell away beneath the sea, a number of natural cyclic processes took place throughout the ages. Movement of shorelines in this process formed the stage on which the drama of the origin of petroleum was enacted.

Fig. 1—*Mountain formed by earth currents.*

The movement in the shoreline of the sea across Texas over the last 250-million-year period is shown in Figs. 2, 3 and 4.

Mountains Are Eroded and Sediments Deposited in the Seas

Elements of the weather — wind, temperature change and rain—have been and are at all times eating away at the mountains and fields. The rock surface is under a continuous process of decay, forming the soil in which vegetation grows. Particles of rock, or the rock cover of soil, are continuously sloughing down slopes to lower levels. Tiny rills with their loads of sediment join into brooks which run into rivers. The greater the slope of the water course, the faster the water runs and the larger will be the size of the particles of sediments that water will transport; therefore, the greater will be the load of sediments carried by the water. Results of a long geologic period of erosion on a mountainous region are illustrated in Fig. 5.

Laden with the products of erosion — mud, silt, sand and gravel — the river runs into the sea where a new process, that

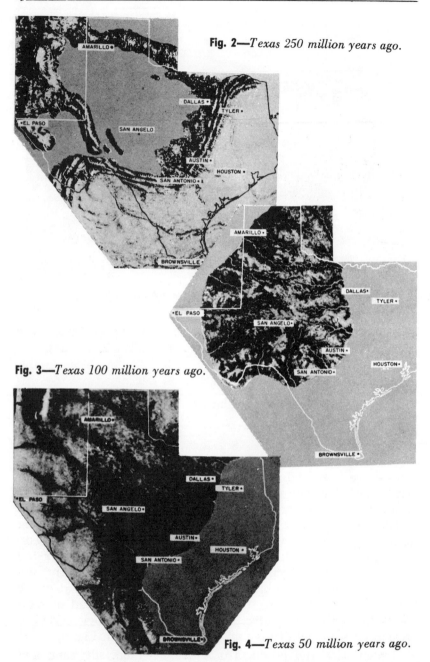

Fig. 2—*Texas 250 million years ago.*

Fig. 3—*Texas 100 million years ago.*

Fig. 4—*Texas 50 million years ago.*

(Courtesy The U. of Texas and Humble Oil & Refining Co.)

Fig. 5—*Mature erosion in a mountain region.*

of deposition, takes place. Products of erosion thus transported to the seas are deposited as soon as the water becomes sufficiently calm to permit the particles to drop to the bottom. The gravels may have come to rest on the river bottom far upstream, perhaps at the foot of the mountain or down stream, depending upon the size and weight of the particles and the velocity of the water. The sands are deposited as offshore sand bars or at the river's mouth as deltas where turbulent wave action carries and distributes the sand particles along the shore (Fig. 6). Silts and muds, being easier to retain in suspension in the water, are carried out to the depths of the sea where they are gently laid down in the calm water far from the shoreline. Advancing and receding movements of shorelines, together with deposits of sands and silts at different points out in the sea, result in separate beds of sands and silts (Figs. 7 and 8).

Petroleum Begins to Form

Although petroleum is known to occur in sediments laid down during all geologic ages, there are many theories concern-

Fig. 6—*Model showing deposition of sand near the river mouth as deltas and along the seashore as sand bars. (Reprinted from* THE EARTH'S CRUST *by L. Dudley Stamp, Crown Publishers, Inc.)*

ing its origin. To study what happened in the dim geologic past, an investigation must be made of what is happening in nature today. The organic theory of the origin of petroleum appears to be the most appropriate explanation based on what is now taking place. This theory conceives that the rivers which carried masses of sediments to the seas also carried great quantities of microscopic plant and animal life. These, together with great volumes of plankton or tiny plant and animal life living in the sea water, settled to the bottom of the sea (Fig. 9). Their remains, covered by sand and silt and sealed from decay, were decomposed by temperature, pressure and bacteria into many hydrocarbon compounds, the mixture of which we know today as petroleum. Proof for the validity of the organic theory stems from the fact that this same process is occurring on a vast scale in contemporary marine deposits.

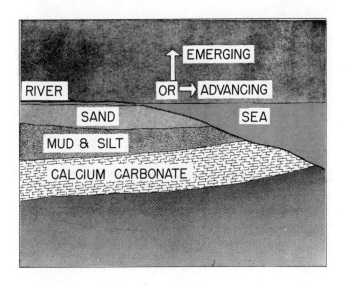

Fig. 7—*Beds formed by emerging or advancing shoreline.*

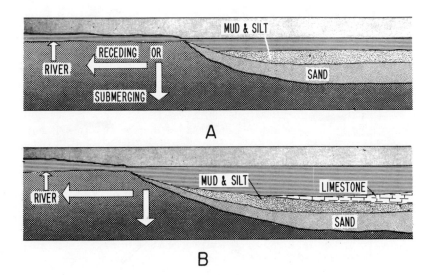

Fig. 8—*Beds formed by submerging or receding shoreline.*

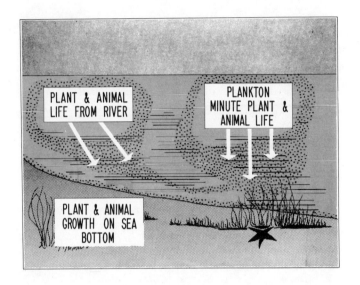

Fig. 9—*Sources of organic material.*

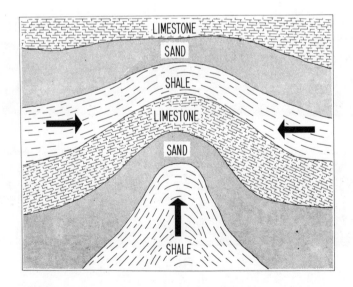

Fig. 10—*Forces of compaction and deformation of beds.*

Structures Form and Sediments
Change into Rock

With the passage of countless centuries, beds of sands and muds became removed from directly beneath the sea because the land raised and the seas retreated. Stresses from the continual shift of the earth's sedimentary crust further compacted the layers of sediments and bent, twisted, broke and further deformed them into many sizes and structural shapes (Fig. 10).

Continuous sedimentation with the moving shoreline buried the earlier deposits under countless tons of other sediments. Great pressure from this overburden tended to squeeze, deform and compact the older layers of sediments. Muds and silts laid down in deep calm sea water were compacted into shales, and then, with geologic time, into slates (Fig. 11). Sands laid down in swift-moving sea waters were cemented by deposition of minerals and clays from the water and compacted into porous sandstones (Fig. 12). In some areas, calcium carbonates were

SILT AT DEPOSITION   SHALE FORMED FROM COMPACTED SILT
A   B

Fig. 11—*Compaction changes silt to shale.*

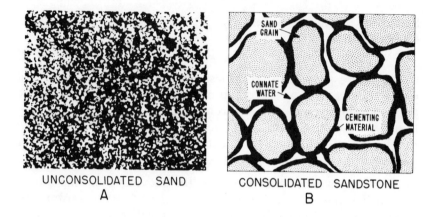

Fig. 12—*Compaction and cementation changes unconsolidated sand to consolidated sandstone.*

laid down in clear waters by precipitation of this mineral from the water or by formation of reefs and beds of the shell remains of sea life. Subsequent earth movements caused these beds, in the presence of mineral-bearing waters, to become compacted into beds of limestone rock. In many cases these beds, because of their hardness and brittleness, became jointed and fractured under the great earth stresses involved. Percolation of water in the existing pore spaces, joints and fractures of the limestone beds caused these pore spaces to be enlarged into "vugs" or "caverns" by solution (Fig. 13). Other waters, carrying mineral concentrations through limestone beds, might fill either the original pore spaces or the solution pore spaces by precipitation. This process is called "secondary deposition".

Petroleum Migrates and Accumulates in Reservoirs

It is not known whether petroleum in the form of oil or gas moved over great or only short distances before accumulating into deposits as we know them today. Neither is it known whether petroleum components were dissolved in the water of the rock or existed as free hydrocarbon mixtures side-by-side

with the water in the rock pore space. The latest belief, however, is that petroleum compounds originated both in the sands
and muds and that rock compaction squeezed them from these
source beds into the pore spaces of the layers of sands and
carbonates where deposits of oil and gas are located today.
Being lighter than the adjacent water, the oil and gas floated
upward through the tiny tortuous pore channels in the sand
until stopped by the overlying dense rock layers. There the oil
and gas could move no further. Sand or limestone rock strata
having connected pore channels through which fluids—oil, gas
or water—can move are said to be "permeable", or to have
"permeability". Rock strata which do not contain connected

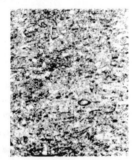

UNCONSOLIDATED
CALCIUM CARBONATES
A

Fig. 13 — *Unconsolidated limestone material at time of deposition and various types of consolidated limestones.*

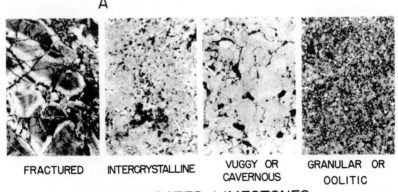

FRACTURED   INTERCRYSTALLINE   VUGGY OR CAVERNOUS   GRANULAR OR OOLITIC

CONSOLIDATED LIMESTONES
B

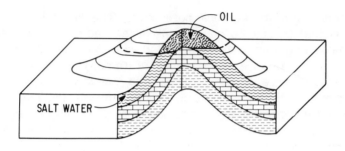

Fig. 14—*Oil accumulated in domal structure.*

pore channels and therefore will not permit fluid movement are said to be impermeable or to have no permeability.

A permeable bed, containing oil and gas in its pore channels, and an overlying bed, which prevents further movement of oil and gas, combine to form a trap. Such a trap can result from a structural condition (flat bed bent upward) or from a stratigraphic condition (lens of permeable rock within an impermeable bed). That portion of a trap in which oil or gas is stored in nature has now come to be referred to generally as a petroleum "reservoir". Often in the past a reservoir has been erroneously referred to as a "pool" of oil because it was thought that oil occurred underground as a lake. Size of a reservoir depends upon size of the trap and how much petroleum is present to accumulate. Many reservoirs are of limited size because the trap was not large enough to contain all petroleum available, while many others are limited because the originally available petroleum was insufficient to fill the trap. In the latter case, the oil and gas

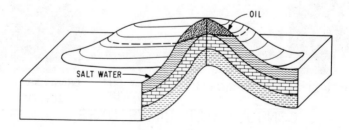

Fig. 15—*Oil accumulation in an anticlinal structure.*

reservoir only partially occupies the trap and water fills the remainder.

Types and Shapes of Reservoirs

Many proposals have been made to classify the different physical shapes of petroleum reservoirs that have been discovered; however, the simplest means of such classification is perhaps a grouping according to the geologic features causing their occurrence. These features are (1) structural folding, (2) structure with faulting, (3) structure with an unconformity, (4) structure caused by some deep-seated movement of earth materials such as salt domes or serpentine plugs, (5) changes in permeability within a formation and (6) combinations of two or more of the foregoing.

Reservoirs formed in folded strata usually result in domes or anticlines (Figs. 14 and 15). These traps were filled by oil

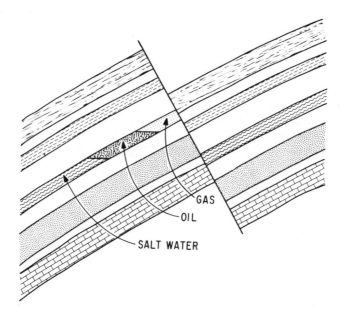

Fig. 16—*Structural trap resulting from faulting.*

moving upward through permeable beds to a point where it was stopped by the impermeable beds on top of the reservoir strata. It is common to find traps partially filled with water where the structure is large enough to hold more oil or gas. Examples of reservoirs formed by anticlinal folding of the structure are the Pegasus field, Midland and Upton Counties, Tex. and the great Azmari Limestone fields of Iran.

Reservoirs formed by faulting occur where escape of oil is prevented by impermeable beds moving into position against the oil-bearing rock on the opposite side of the fault plane. The oil is held in traps of this type by the structural dip of the bed and the faulting (Fig. 16). Reservoirs of this type are typified by the Mt. Poso field, Kern County, Calif. and the Luling, Mexia and Talco fields in Central Texas.

Another type of reservoir is one formed as a result of an unconformity where upward escape of oil has been stopped by the impermeable material laid down on the weathered surface of the lower beds (Fig. 17). The East Texas field is formed in this manner.

Accumulations of oil are found in sediments on or surrounding material such as salt or serpentine plugs that have pierced and deformed the overlying strata (Figs. 18 and 19). Examples

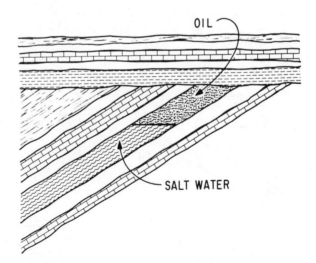

Fig. 17—*Oil accumulation under an unconformity.*

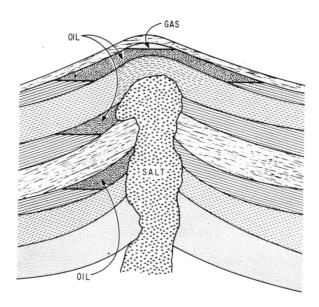

Fig. 18—*Oil accumulation in the vicinity of a piercement-type salt dome.*

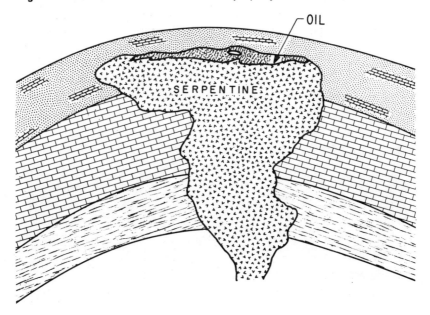

Fig. 19—*Oil accumulation in areas of porosity in a serpentine plug.*

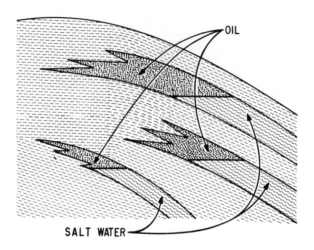

Fig. 20—*Oil accumulation in sand lenses of the sand bar type.*

of salt dome fields are the Spindletop field, Jefferson County, Tex. and the Avery Island field, Iberia Parish, La. Examples of serpentine plug fields are the Lytton Springs field in Caldwell County, Tex. and the Hilbig field, Bastrop County, Tex.

Another type of trap is one that is closed by variation in permeability within the strata (Figs. 20 and 21). The size of oil and gas deposits in reservoirs of this type is governed by the manner in which the beds were laid down rather than by structural closure. In this case, oil is held in place within per-

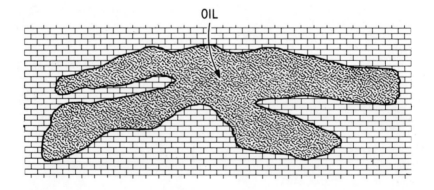

Fig. 21—*Oil accumulation in porous zones in limestone.*

meable segments of the bed which are surrounded by impermeable segments of the same bed. Fields having sand reservoirs
of this type are the Goose Creek field in Harris County, Tex.
and the Sprayberry field in West Texas. Limestone reservoirs
of this type are exemplified by the East Dundas field, Richland
and Jasper Counties, Ill. (which produce from McClosky limestone) and the Scurry Area Canyon Reef (SACROC) field in
Scurry County, Tex. (which produces from a reef section).

Perhaps the most common type of reservoir is one that is
formed not by a single structural feature alone, but instead, by
a combination of folding, faulting, changes in permeability or
other conditions. Examples of reservoirs of this nature are the
many reservoirs found in the Seeligson-Tijerina Canales Blucher-
La Gloria trend of fields in Southwest Texas and the Wilmington
field, Los Angeles County, Calif.

♦

♦

♦

C H A P T E R   2

Characteristics of Reservoir Rocks

The grains making up sandstones are all irregular in shape. The degree of irregularity, or lack of roundness, evidences as to how the sand grains may have been formed originally or the degree to which they subsequently have eroded. Violent crushing or grinding action between rocks causes grains to be very irregular and sharp-edged. Tumbling action of grains along the bottom of streams or seas smooths sand grains. Wind-blown sand, as occurs in moving dunes of the great deserts, results in sand grains that are even more rounded (Fig. 22). Sand grains that make up sandstone beds and fragments of carbonate materials that make up limestone beds usually never fit together perfectly even though overburden rock pressure on these beds may be quite great. The void space created throughout the beds between grains is called pore space.

The pore spaces in reservoir rock, sometimes called interstices, provide the containers for the accumulation of oil and gas deposits (Figs. 12 and 13). Pore space, or porosity, in rock gives the rock its characteristic ability to absorb and hold fluids. Most commercial reservoirs of oil and gas occur in sandstone, limestone or dolomite rocks; however, some reservoirs occur in fractured shale. Knowledge of the physical characteristics of the pore spaces and of the rock itself (which controls the character-

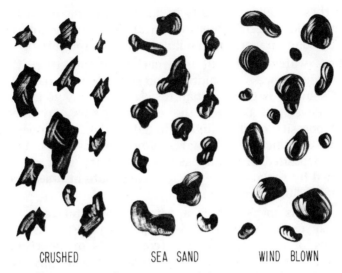

CRUSHED   SEA SAND   WIND BLOWN

Fig. 22—*Shapes of sand grains created by various types of erosion.*

istics of the pore spaces) is of vital importance in understanding the nature of a given reservoir.

Porosity

As sand was laid down in geologically ancient seas, the first fluid that filled pore spaces in the sand was sea water or "connate" water. Some pore spaces became isolated, but the vast majority in sandstones containing petroleum deposits remained interconnected and have had water in them or moving through them throughout their existence. One method of classifying reservoir rocks, therefore, is based on whether pore spaces in which the oil and gas is found originated when the formation was laid down or whether they were formed through subsequent earth stresses or ground water action. The first type of porosity is termed "original porosity" and the latter, "secondary porosity". Most sandstone porosity is original while most limestones and dolomites owe their porosity to secondary formation.

Secondary porosity in limestone beds occurred as a result of fracturing, jointing, solution, recrystallization or a combination of these. Original porosity in limestone is important because such must have been present when artesian water entered and began its solution work on the limestone rock formation.

Where water is present in a carbonate formation, there is a continuous process of solution and deposition or recrystallization. If solution is greater than deposition in any zone, porosity will be developed between the crystal grains. An important type of porosity of this kind is found in dolomite zones which occur in conjunction with large limestone deposits. Dolomite may be deposited originally as a sedimentary rock, or it may be formed by replacing the calcium carbonate in limestone rock with magnesium carbonate.

Porosity is measured as a per cent of total rock volume. The most useful way to classify porosity (Fig. 23) is into categories of effective porosity (continuous or interconnected porosity), non-effective porosity (discontinuous or isolated porosity), and total porosity (the sum of all the porosity). Only effective porosity has real significance in rocks containing

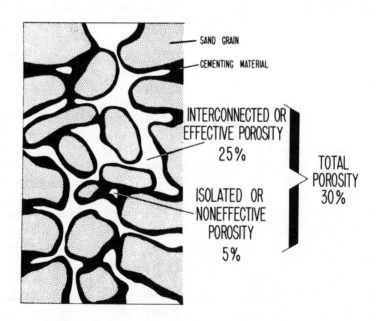

Fig. 23—*Effective, non-effective and total porosity.*

present-day commercial oil and gas deposits because it is only from this type of porosity that the fluids can move and be recovered.

Permeability

The ease with which fluid can move through the interconnected pore spaces of the rock denotes the degree of permeability possessed by the rock. The rock is more or less permeable depending upon whether the rock will let fluid pass through it with greater or less ease. This is similar to pipe lines where larger or straighter lines let fluid move through more easily. Many rocks are impervious to movement of water, oil or gas even though they may actually be quite porous. Some of these are clays, shales, chalk, anhydrite and some highly cemented sandstones.

When considering the permeability of rock, we immediately must think in terms of the force which makes fluid flow through the rock. Such force is pressure—just as in a pipe where a pressure is applied to force liquid or gas to move through the pipe. In 1856, the French engineer Henry Darcy performed tests on water filters, and some of this work provided the engineering profession with the relation which permits measurement and study of the ease of fluid flow through

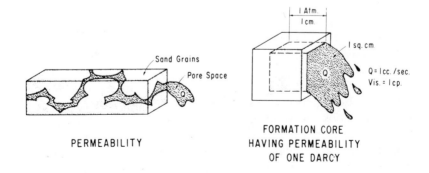

PERMEABILITY

FORMATION CORE
HAVING PERMEABILITY
OF ONE DARCY

Fig. 24—*Fluid flow in permeable sand.*

porous rock. Darcy's law of fluid flow states that rate of flow through a given rock varies directly according to some numerical quantity and the pressure applied, and varies inversely according to the viscosity of the fluid flowing. The numerical quantity is the permeability and is measured in darcies. A sandstone having 1 darcy of permeability is defined as one that 1 cubic centimeter of fluid of 1 centipoise viscosity (or the viscosity of water at 68°F) would flow each second through a portion of the sand 1 centimeter in length and having 1 square centimeter of area through which to move if the pressure drop across the sand is 14.7 pounds per square inch (or equivalent to atmospheric pressure), as shown in Fig. 24.

Reservoir rock having an average permeability as great as 1 darcy is found in only a small portion of the reservoirs containing petroleum deposits. The usual measure of rock permeability, therefore, is in millidarcies (md) or thousandths of a darcy.

The magnitude of permeability, in terms of oil production from a reservoir rock into a well, is illustrated by the fact that a reservoir rock 10-feet thick having 1 darcy of effective permeability will permit about 150 barrels of oil per day to flow into a wellbore if the pressure in the well is 10 pounds per square inch below the pressure out in the reservoir.

Factors that Influence Porosity and Permeability

Porosity and permeability of sandstone depend upon many factors, among which are size and shape of the grains, variations in size of grains, arrangement in which grains were laid down and compacted, and amount of clay and other materials which cement the sand grains together.

Sizes of the sand grains which make up a rock do not influence the amount of porosity occurring in the rock. However variations in sand-grain sizes do influence considerably the per cent of porosity. An example is shown in Fig. 25 where porosity between spheres of 1-inch diameter is the same as porosity between spheres of ½-inch diameter, provided the spheres are arranged in the same manner. If they are arranged in cubic order, porosity is about 48 per cent; whereas if they

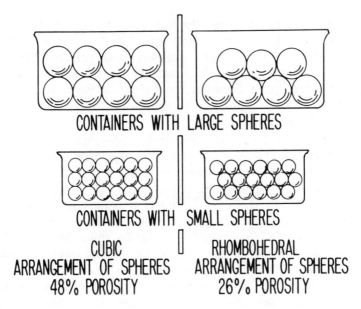

CONTAINERS WITH LARGE SPHERES

CONTAINERS WITH SMALL SPHERES

CUBIC
ARRANGEMENT OF SPHERES
48% POROSITY

RHOMBOHEDRAL
ARRANGEMENT OF SPHERES
26% POROSITY

Fig. 25—*Effects of size and arrangement of spheres on porosity.*

are arranged in rhombohedral order, porosity is about 26 per cent. If spheres of varying sizes are packed together, porosity may be any amount from 48 per cent to a very small amount approaching 0 per cent as shown in Fig. 26. This principle is illustrated in mixing concrete where the basic materials are gravel mixed with sand, with the resulting mixture having very little porosity and requiring only a small amount of cement and water to fill the remaining pore space completely.

To illustrate variation in porosity and permeability with a given type of sand grain, various features are considered separately. If the sand grains are elongated or flat and are packed with their flat surfaces together, porosity and permeability may both be low. Permeability along the flat surfaces will be higher, however, than the permeability in a direction that is perpendicular to, or across, the flat surfaces of the grains. In a reservoir, the permeability horizontal with the bed is usually higher than the permeability vertical across the bed because the process of sedimentation, where the sand grains are washed to their final position, causes the grains to be laid down with their flattest sides in a horizontal position.

If sand grains of generally flat proportions are laid down with the flat sides non-uniformly positioned and located in indiscriminate directions, both porosity and permeability may be very high (Fig. 27). To illustrate, if bricks are stacked properly, pore space between the bricks is very small; yet if the same bricks are piled indiscriminately, space between the bricks might be quite large.

The shape and size of sand grains are important features that determine the size of the openings between the sand grains. If the grains are elongated, large and uniformly arranged with the longest dimension horizontal, permeability to fluid flow through the pore channels will be quite large horizontally and medium-to-large vertically. If the grains are more uniformly rounded, permeability will be quite large in both directions and more nearly the same. Permeability is found generally to be lower with smaller grain size if other factors are not influential. This occurs because the pore channels become smaller as the size of the grains is reduced, and it is more difficult for fluid to flow through the smaller channels (Fig. 28).

Sandstones are compacted and cemented together with clays

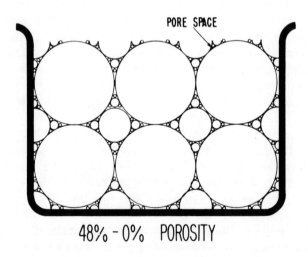

48% - 0% POROSITY

Fig. 26—*Effect of variations in size of spheres on porosity.*

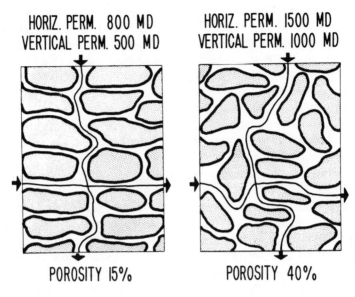

HORIZ. PERM. 800 MD
VERTICAL PERM. 500 MD

HORIZ. PERM. 1500 MD
VERTICAL PERM. 1000 MD

POROSITY 15%

POROSITY 40%

Fig. 27—*Variations in porosity and permeability with sand grain arrangement.*

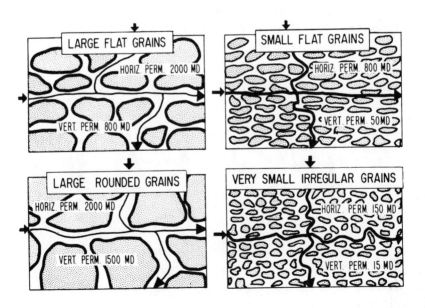

LARGE FLAT GRAINS
HORIZ. PERM. 2000 MD
VERT. PERM. 800 MD

SMALL FLAT GRAINS
HORIZ. PERM. 800 MD
VERT. PERM. 50MD

LARGE ROUNDED GRAINS
HORIZ. PERM. 2000 MD
VERT. PERM. 1500 MD

VERY SMALL IRREGULAR GRAINS
HORIZ. PERM. 150 MD
VERT. PERM. 15 MD

Fig. 28—*Effects of shape and size of sand grains on permeability.*

and minerals. Porosity and permeability of a sandstone are both influenced to a marked degree by the amount of cementing material present in the pore channels and the way this material occupies the pore space between the sand grains (Fig. 29). This is true because the cementing material may be uniformly located along the pore channels to somewhat reduce both porosity and permeability; or, the cementing material may be located so as to congest only the pore openings, where a small amount can reduce permeability drastically while leaving the porosity quite high.

Limestones, except for the granular oolitic type which may be similar in character to sandstone, are composed of more densely spaced particles and depend for porosity upon space between microscopic crystals in the rock, solution void spaces caused by movement and solvent action of ground waters, and other spaces formed by fractures and joints caused by earth stresses. Porosity and permeability, however, have the same meaning in limestone as in sandstone, although they are usually extremely irregular and much more difficult to measure and analyze.

Thin sections and impregnated sections of samples of three sandstones from the Waltersburg, Weber and Woodbine forma-

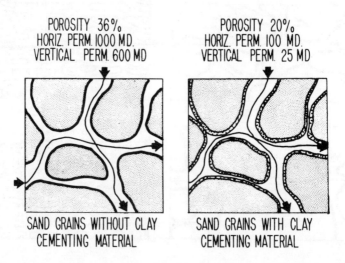

PROSITY 36%
HORIZ. PERM. 1000 MD.
VERTICAL PERM. 600 MD

POROSITY 20%
HORIZ. PERM. 100 MD.
VERTICAL PERM. 25 MD

SAND GRAINS WITHOUT CLAY
CEMENTING MATERIAL

SAND GRAINS WITH CLAY
CEMENTING MATERIAL

Fig. 29—*Effects of clay cementing material on porosity and permeability.*

tions are shown in Fig. 30. The thin sections show size and distribution of the grains, and the other sections are impregnated with Woods metal, then polished to show size and distribution of the pore spaces. The Waltersburg sand has smaller grains and pore channels than the Weber, but there are more pore channels volume-wise. Thus, porosity is greater in the Waltersburg than the Weber. On the other hand, pore channels in the Weber are larger than those in the Waltersburg; therefore, permeability in the Weber is much greater. Woodbine grains and pore channels are much larger than the other sands shown. The porosity of the Woodbine is greater because of the presence of less packing and less cementing material. Permeability is very high because the pore channels are large and less cementing material is present to impede fluid flow.

In summary, the amount of porosity is principally determined by shape and arrangement of sand grains and the amount of cementing material present, whereas permeability depends largely on size of the pore openings and the degree and type of cementation between sand grains. Although many formations show a correlation between porosity and permeability, the several factors influencing these characteristics may differ widely in effect, producing rock having no correlation between porosity and permeability.

Relative Permeability

Permeability is the measure of the ease with which a fluid flows through connecting pore spaces of a reservoir rock. Because not one, but three fluids—gas, oil and water—can flow in petroleum reservoirs, another type of permeability must be considered. When dealing with the flow of more than one fluid through a sand, one must consider relative permeability relationships—the ease with which one fluid, of the two or more fluids present, will flow through connecting pore spaces in the presence of each other as compared to the ease with which one fluid will flow when it alone is present.

Consider an oil reservoir at high pressure (Fig. 31A). Gas

THIN SECTION   IMPREGNATED SECTION

0   0.5   I
MILLIMETERS

POR. = 18.6 %
PERM. = 25 MD.

WALTERSBURG   SAND

POR.= 17.6 %
PERM.= 220 MD.

WEBER   SAND

POR. = 25.6 %
PERM. = 4400 MD.

WOODBINE   SAND

Fig. 30—*Grain structure shown by thin section and porosity shown by impregnated section of three sandstones. (Courtesy* BULLETIN OF AAPG—*Feb., 1952.)*

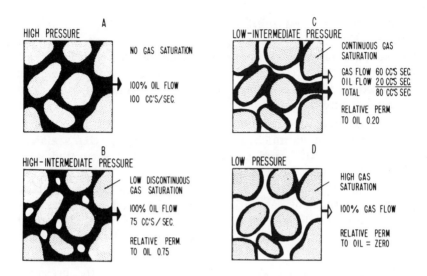

Fig. 31—*Concept of relative permeability showing that a change in the amount of a fluid present in the pore channels will change the rate at which that fluid flows relative to the rate it would flow if only that fluid were present.*

has not been allowed to come out of solution (Chapter 3); therefore, all available space is filled with oil, and only oil is flowing. If reservoir pressure is allowed to decline, some lighter components of the oil will evolve and collect as gas in the pore space crevices between sand grains (Fig. 31B).

If the pressure decline is slight, then the gas that forms will not be sufficient to form a continuous pore-to-pore gas saturation; still only oil can flow from the pore spaces. Gas, though it does not flow, slows down the flow of oil by its presence. If reservoir pressure is further reduced, the small bubbles of gas in each pore will grow in size until a continuous gas phase is established along the pore network (Fig. 31C). Production then will be oil and gas. The per cent of gas saturation in the pore space at the time when gas starts to flow is termed "equilibrium gas saturation" and differs somewhat in different sands because of variations in sand pore space configuration.

As pressure continues to decline, or as the gas saturation continues to increase, more and more gas and less and less oil flow in the sand until finally almost 100 per cent gas is flowing (Fig. 31D). Relative permeability, then, can be defined as the rate of flow of one fluid (such as oil) through pore channels in the presence of a second fluid (such as gas) as compared to the rate of flow if, under the same pressure drop conditions, only the one fluid were present.

For example, if the amount of oil flowing in Fig. 31B is only 75 per cent as much as that flowing in Fig. 31A, relative permeability of the sand to oil, with the sand saturated with the percentages of oil and gas shown in Fig. 31B, is 0.75. The flow of oil in Fig. 31C may be reduced to 20 per cent; thus, at the conditions of saturation shown the sand would have a relative permeability to oil of 0.20. Relative permeability to oil is zero where oil saturation has been decreased to a minimum (Fig. 31D).

This same principal governs the flow of gas in the presence of either water or oil. The amount of each fluid present, making up the saturation condition of the pore spaces, will control the ease of fluid movement and thus the relative permeability relationship of the reservoir rock. This relationship is a function of the configuration of the rock pore spaces and the wetting characteristics of the fluids and rock surfaces.

♦

♦

♦

CHAPTER 3

Characteristics of
Oil and Gas

Nearly all naturally occurring petroleum deposits are made up of an extremely large number of petroleum compounds, all mixed together. Molecules of all these compounds are composed of the chemical elements hydrogen and carbon in various proportions. Petroleum compounds of these elements are called hydrocarbons, and each compound is made up of a different proportion of the two elements. Seldom are two crude oils found that are seemingly identical and certainly never are two crude oils made up of the same proportions of the various compounds. Within a single petroleum deposit, the mixture differs some from place to place and in many cases to an extreme degree.

Components of Petroleum

The vast number of hydrocarbon compounds making up petroleum have been grouped chemically into series of compounds. Each series consists of those compounds similar in their molecular make-up and characteristics. Within a given series there exist compounds from extremely light, or chemically simple, to heavy, or chemically complex. As an analogy, the hydrocarbons may be compared to cattle; just as cattle are classified into different breeds, hydrocarbons are classified into different series. Just as there are a multitude of different size cattle within a breed, so within a hydrocarbon series there are a multitude of compounds that differ because of the weight of the molecules of which they are made.

The most common and greatest number of hydrocarbon compounds making up a naturally occurring petroleum deposit are those of the paraffin series, which includes methane, ethane, propane, butane and others (Figs. 32 and 33). Because of this, it has been the practice in the petroleum producing industry to analyze all petroleum samples according to their fractional composition based on the boiling properties of the various paraffin series constituents.

The composition of most petroleum deposits will include some quantity of nearly all components throughout the entire range of weights and complexities, whether the hydrocarbon is heavy crude oil with characteristics approaching tar, or the lightest of natural gases from which liquids can be condensed only with great difficulty. Gas, therefore, is not a gas because it is composed entirely of light molecules which are different from those making up crude oil. Naturally occurring gas is

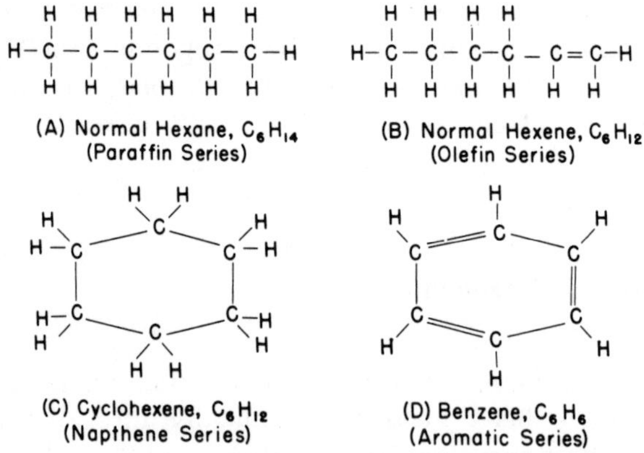

(A) Normal Hexane, C_6H_{14}
(Paraffin Series)

(B) Normal Hexene, C_6H_{12}
(Olefin Series)

(C) Cyclohexene, C_6H_{12}
(Napthene Series)

(D) Benzene, C_6H_6
(Aromatic Series)

Fig. 32—*Structural formulas of four hydrocarbon series (compounds containing six carbon atoms).*

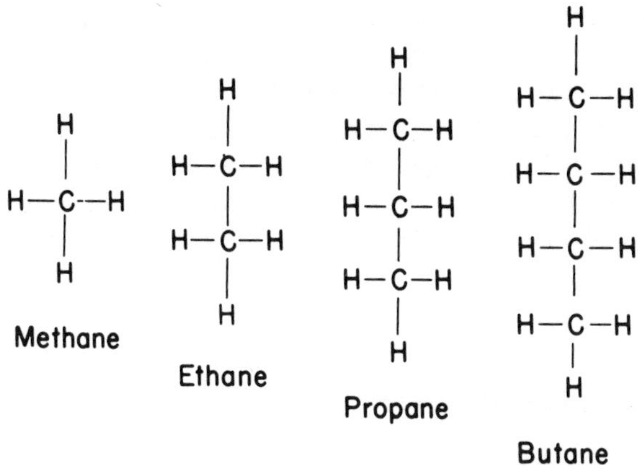

Fig. 33—*Structural formulas of four lightest paraffin compounds.*

different because the majority of its component molecules are lighter and simpler, whereas liquid crude oil is made up of a majority of the heavier and more complex component molecules. Both natural gas and crude oil, however, contain some of most all existing hydrocarbon components.

Phases of Petroleum

Because of man's environment of earth, water and air, it could well have been that his first scientific observations were that matter existed in three states or forms—solid, liquid and gas. Generally it is found that all substances may exist in any of the three forms which have been termed phases of matter.

Whether a substance exists in a solid, liquid or gas phase will be determined by temperature and pressure conditions acting on the substance. It is well known that steam can be changed to water by lowering its temperature and water can be changed into ice by further lowering its temperature. Hydrocarbon compounds, either individually or in mixtures, will change their state or phase in the same way—by changing their temperature and pressure. The resulting change is called "phase behavior".

Heavy hydrocarbons, including paraffins and tars, sometimes form naturally as solids in the reservoir and present problems in oil production operations; however, this does not often happen, and such problems will not be discussed herein. The scope of this book will be limited to behavior of hydrocarbons as they change from gas to liquid and liquid to gas and the operating problems and their control caused by such changes.

Molecular Behavior

Hydrocarbons behave peculiarly when their pressure and temperature are changed. This behavior is best explained by the behavior of the individual molecules making up the mixture. Four physical factors are important in governing the behavior of hydrocarbon matter. These are (1) pressure, (2) molecular attraction, (3) kinetic energy (molecular motion associated with temperature) and (4) molecular repulsion (Fig. 34).

Pressure and molecular attraction tend to confine molecules or pull them together so that the greater the value of these forces, the greater the tendency for the material to become more dense, as is the case when gases become liquid.

Molecular attraction is considered an internal pressure since it is within the system and acts on the molecules in the same

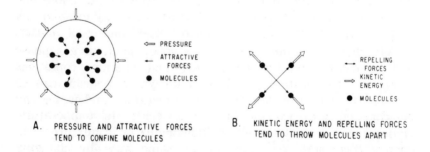

A. PRESSURE AND ATTRACTIVE FORCES TEND TO CONFINE MOLECULES

B. KINETIC ENERGY AND REPELLING FORCES TEND TO THROW MOLECULES APART

Fig. 34—*Forces governing hydrocarbon behavior.*

way as external pressure. Attractive force between molecules changes with distances between the molecules, the force increasing as the distance between the molecules decreases; it differs with the mass of molecules, the force increasing as the mass of the molecules increases.

Kinetic energy, or molecular motion, increases as temperature increases so that the greater the temperature of a material, the greater the tendency for the material to be thrown apart and thus decrease in density or change from a liquid to a gas (or for a gas to expand).

When molecules get so close together that their electronic fields overlap, a repelling force is present that tends to increase the resistance of the material to further compression. When hydrocarbon material appears to be at rest (not expanding, contracting in volume or changing state), the forces tending to confine the molecules balance forces tending to throw them apart and the material is considered to be in equilibrium.

Changes in Phases

If pressure is increased, molecules are forced closer together so that gas will be compressed or change to a liquid. However, as pressure is decreased, the reverse occurs—gas expands and liquid tends to vaporize to gas. The molecules in the latter case are thrown apart by their own kinetic energy, and molecular repulsion. These phase changes caused by changes in pressure are termed normal or regular behavior.

If the molecules are smaller, as in the case of methane and ethane, there is less attraction between molecules and greater tendency for them to be thrown apart by their kinetic energy into gas; whereas, if molecules are larger, as in hexane and heptane, they tend to be attracted together into the liquid rather than thrown into the gaseous state by their kinetic energies. As the temperature of the compounds increases, kinetic energy increases. The tendency then is for all molecules in the liquid state to be thrown into the gaseous state and for gases to expand. However, if temperature decreased, the kinetic energy decreases, and all molecules (even the lighter molecules) tend to be attracted together into a liquid state and even frozen into the solid state if the temperature is low enough. This behavior is also considered normal or regular.

Pure Hydrocarbons

For a single or pure hydrocarbon such as propane, butane or pentane, there is a given pressure for every temperature at which the hydrocarbon can exist both as a liquid and a gas. This is demonstrated in Fig. 35. Under these conditions, the forces which tend to pull the molecules closer together (pressure and attractive forces) balance the kinetic energy which tends to throw them apart. If pressure is increased without a temperature change, the gas molecules are forced closer together and the attractive forces between molecules are thus increased. The forces then tending to pull molecules together are greater than the kinetic energy, and the molecules condense to a liquid state.

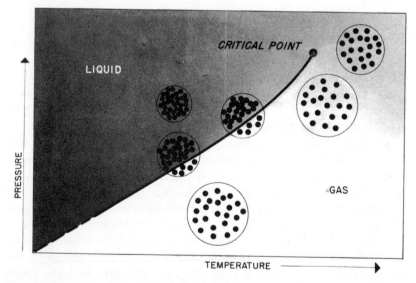

Fig. 35—*Vapor pressure vs temperature for a pure hydrocarbon component. (Courtesy* WORLD OIL—*March, 1953.)*

However, if pressure is decreased without a temperature change, the distance between gas molecules is increased and the attractive forces are thus decreased. Forces tending to pull the molecules together are then less than the kinetic energy, and the molecules disperse into a gas.

Actually, pressure results from the molecular bombardment of the containing vessel and liquid surface. The increase in volume tends to reduce the pressure by increasing the distance molecules must move to strike the container. As temperature increases, kinetic energy is increased; higher pressures are required for existence of the balanced conditions at which the two phases can exist simultaneously.

The curve (Fig. 35) plotted through the pressure-temperature points where two phases exist is called the "vapor-pressure curve". There is a temperature above which the material will not exist in two phases regardless of the pressure. This is called the "critical point", and temperature and pressure at this point are called "critical temperature" and "critical pressure".

It is common practice to consider the material as a gas

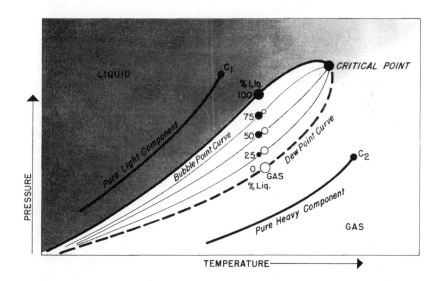

Fig. 36—*Vapor pressure curves for two pure components and phase diagram for a 50:50 mixture of the same components.*
(Courtesy WORLD OIL—*March, 1953.)*

when it exists at temperature and pressure conditions below the vapor-pressure curve and as a liquid above the vapor-pressure curve. Such a definition obviously is confusing because ranges of temperature and pressure exist in which the material can be classified as either liquid or gas. These ranges are shown in the upper right-hand portion of Fig. 35. In these ranges, the temperature is so great that attractive forces between the molecules are not sufficiently great to permit them to coalesce to a liquid phase because of the higher kinetic energy of molecules at the high temperature condition. Under these temperature conditions, an increase in pressure causes the molecules to move together uniformly as pressure is increased. This confusion is minimized when working with reservoirs because reservoir temperature (and thus the temperature of the hydrocarbons in the reservoir) usually remains constant; therefore, only pressure and volume are usually altered to an appreciable degree in the reservoir during production.

Hydrocarbon Mixtures

In a mixture of two components, the system is no longer so simple in its behavior as the one-component, or pure, substance. Instead of a single line representing the pressure-temperature relationship, there is a broad region in which two phases (liquid and gas) co-exist. Fig. 36 is a diagrammatic correlation, or phase diagram, of the phase behavior of a 50:50 mixture of two hydrocarbons such as propane and heptane. Superimposed on the correlation are vapor-pressure curves of the two components in their pure state.

The two-phase region of the phase diagram is bounded on one side by a bubble-point line and on the other by a dew-point line, with the two lines joining at the critical point. A bubble point occurs where gas begins to leave solution in oil with decreasing pressure, while a dew point is reached when liquid begins to condense from gas with either decreasing or increasing pressure. Of importance is the fact that, for a given temperature, the pressure at which a mixture of two components is condensed to total liquid is lower than the pressure at which the lighter component in the mixture would condense if it were not in the mixture. The pressure at which the mixture of two components is vaporized to total gas is higher than the pressure at which the heavy component would vaporize if it were not in the mixture. This is caused by the attractive forces between molecules of like and unlike sizes. Attraction of the heavy for light molecules pulls the light material into the liquid at a lower imposed pressure than would the light molecules among themselves in the absence of the heavy molecules. Attraction of the light for heavy molecules pulls the heavy material into a gas at a higher imposed pressure than would the heavy molecules among themselves in the absence of light molecules.

At the critical point, properties of both gas and liquid mixtures are identical. It is significant that the definition of critical point, as applied to a single-component system, no longer applies because both liquid and gas phases exist at temperatures and pressures above the critical point, although the degree may be slight in a system of only two components. As the system be-

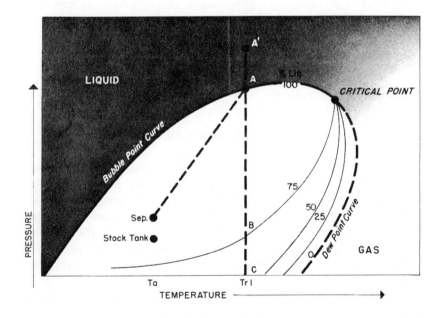

Fig. 37—*Phase diagram of low shrinkage oil.*

comes more complex with a greater number of different components, the pressure and temperature ranges in which two phases exist increase greatly.

An idealized pressure-temperature phase diagram of a common, naturally occurring petroleum is shown in Fig. 37. If the oil existed at its bubble point or if the original reservoir pressure was the saturation pressure of the mixture, the petroleum would be existing at A. If the pressure of this same oil should be at A , the oil would be undersaturated. Separator and stock tank temperatures and pressures are indicated. Quantities of liquid and gas represented by location of the stock tank point on the diagram, however, do not indicate what would occur in the stock tank because the original mixture changes at the separator in the oil and gas production process.

Vertical or constant temperature line A-B represents the path the material takes into the two-phase region as pressure is dropped at reservoir temperature and represents quantities of liquid and gas existing in equilibrium at temperature and pressure conditions represented by the given location of the point in the phase loop. This is physically represented in the reservoir by gas coming out of solution, the amount of which is governed by the amount of drop in pressure.

Equilibrium Separation

Low Shrinkage Oil

A given volume of oil existing at its bubble point at reservoir temperature is considered to be saturated with gas at the given temperature and pressure conditions. Thus the term "saturation pressure" is synonymous with bubble-point pressure at a given temperature. A decrease in pressure will cause the original sample to change into two phases as shown by Fig. 38. The physical change is evidenced as gas being liberated from the liquid.

It is a common misbelief that a certain amount of gas is dissolved in oil and that a pressure drop results in the gas coming out of solution. Actually, the first gas liberated is composed prin-

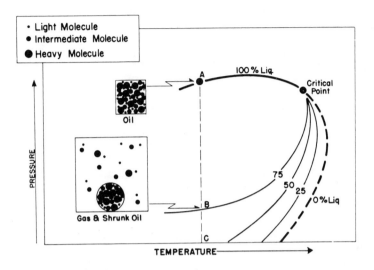

Fig. 38—*Equilibrium vaporization of low shrinkage oil.*

cipally of the lightest components (methane, ethane and propane) because these components possess the highest molecular energy and the lowest molecular attraction for other molecules.

Vaporization of the lighter components is usually followed by quantities of heavier components until some low pressure is reached where only a fraction of the original materials remains liquid. Portions of all the component materials (including heavy components) have gone into the gas phase with, of course, a greater percentage of the lightest materials composing the gas. The gas formed has done so by vaporization of the light components and, as a result, the remaining liquid is described as having shrunk in volume. This change is illustrated in Fig. 38 for a typical low shrinkage oil, or one that shrinks only a small amount.

For low shrinkage oil, there is a somewhat uniform change in shrinkage as pressure drops through the high and intermediate pressure range (A to B, Fig. 37 and A to B on the low shrinkage oil curve in Fig. 39). This shrinkage occurs principally as a result of volumetric loss of light materials. It increases rapidly, however, through the low pressure range (B to C, Figs. 37 and 39). This shrinkage occurs principally through volumetric loss

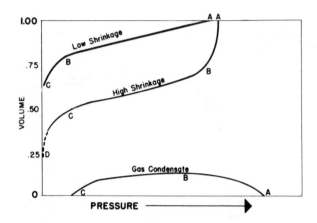

Fig. 39—*Equilibrium shrinkage of hydrocarbon liquids.*

of intermediate and heavy material from the remaining liquid. Shrinkage characteristics in this range of pressures are extremely significant because surface separation of oil from gas occurs under these conditions.

Increasing shrinkage at low pressure is caused by kinetic energy of the heavy liquid molecules being greater than attractive forces within the liquid under these reduced pressure conditions.

High Shrinkage Oils

Certain oils are known as high shrinkage oils because their shrinkage with pressure reduction is greater than normal. The term "high shrinkage" is qualitative because there is no distinct set of conditions by which low and high shrinkage oils may be classified. Higher shrinkage is usually brought about because of the existence of greater quantities of intermediate components or lesser quantities of heavy components in the mixture.

Changes in oil shrinkage by vaporization of material through pressure reduction is illustrated by temperature condition Tr2 in the phase diagram in Fig. 40 and the high shrinkage curve in Fig. 39.

Behavior of high shrinkage oil in the high pressure range is different from that of low shrinkage oil. As pressure drops slightly from saturation pressure (A to B), not only do the light component molecules leave solution, but a large quantity of intermediates also leave solution to form gas. Actually, it is the presence of this large quantity of intermediate components that makes a high shrinkage oil. High shrinkage of the oil from A to B is caused not only by attraction of intermediate component liquid molecules to closely spaced, light component gas molecules, but also by the normally high kinetic energy of the intermediate component liquid molecules.

As pressure drops further (B to C), the attraction for intermediate component liquid molecules by light component gas molecules decreases because of an increase in the distance separating them; therefore, there is a tendency toward greater attraction between the remaining liquid intermediates to liquid heavies, which prevents further rapid vaporization throughout the middle pressure range. Vaporizing tendency of heavy component liquid molecules increases through the low pressure range (C to D) just as in the case of low shrinkage oils, although to a greater degree because of the greater quantity of intermediates held by

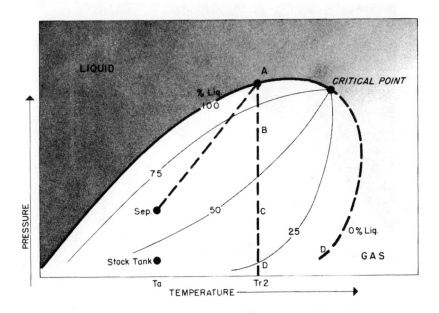

Fig. 40—*Phase diagram of high shrinkage oil.*

attraction to the heavy liquid molecules until the low pressure condition is reached. High shrinkage oils behave similarly to low shrinkage oils in the low pressure range except that shrinkage is much greater. Shrinkage characteristics of high shrinkage oils are, therefore, of great significance in surface separation problems.

Retrograde Condensate Gas

Some hydrocarbon mixtures exist naturally above their critical temperature as gas condensates. When pressure is decreased on these mixtures, instead of expanding (if a gas) or vaporizing (if a liquid) as might be expected, they tend to condense. Conversely, when pressure is increased, they vaporize instead of condensing. The process is illustrated by temperature condition Tr3 in Fig. 41 and the gas condensate curve in Fig. 39. This process is caused by forces acting on molecules of unlike sizes and depends upon a balance of these forces, as illustrated in Fig. 42. Normal vaporization and condensation, on the other

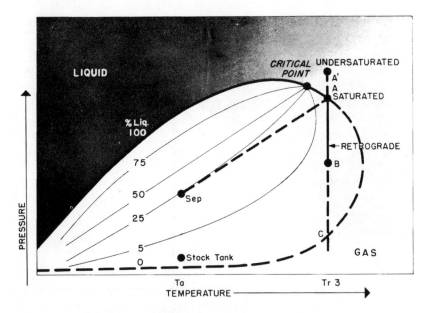

Fig. 41—*Phase diagram of retrograde condensate gas.*
(Courtesy WORLD OIL—*March, 1953.)*

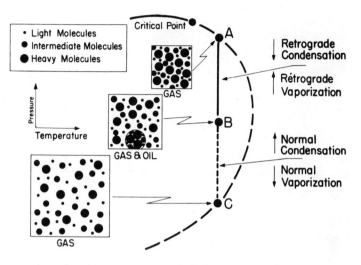

Fig. 42—*Equilibrium retrograde behavior of condensate gas.*
(Courtesy WORLD OIL—*March, 1953.)*

hand, depend more upon balance between molecular forces of like-size component molecules.

As pressure drops (at constant temperature) below dew-point pressure (A), the attraction between light and heavy component molecules decreases because the light molecules move farther apart. As this occurs, attraction between the heavy component molecules becomes more effective; thus, tnese heavy molecules coalesce into a liquid. This process continues until a pressure (B) is reached where a maximum amount of liquid is formed. Further reduction in pressure permits the heavy molecules to commence normal vaporization—the process whereby fewer gas molecules strike the liquid surface; this causes more molecules to leave than to enter the liquid phase, until complete vaporization of the liquid again occurs (C).

Wet Gas

Behavior of a wet gas is shown in Fig. 43 where temperature is above the critical condensing temperature of the gas mixture. Therefore, a reduction of pressure (from A to B) will not cause liquid condensation. Passage of gas from existing temperature

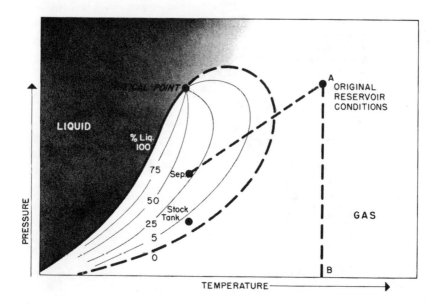

Fig. 43—*Phase diagram of wet gas. (Courtesy* WORLD OIL—*March, 1953.)*

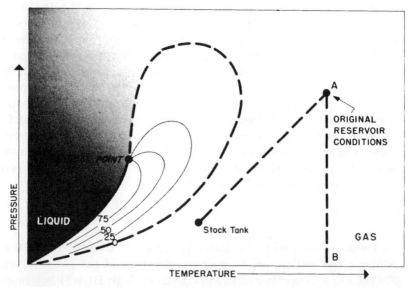

Fig. 44—*Phase diagram of dry gas. (Courtesy* WORLD OIL—*March, 1953.)*

to stock tank conditions where the temperature is lower, however, will result in the formation of liquid. This is caused by a sufficient decrease in the kinetic energy of heavy molecules with temperature drop and their subsequent change to liquid through the attractive forces between molecules.

Dry Gas

Behavior of a dry gas is illustrated by the phase loop in Fig. 44. The temperature is above the critical condensing temperature of the gas mixture and, like the wet gas, will not condense to a liquid with pressure drop (from A to B). Passage of dry gas to surface conditions will not, however, result in a condensation of liquid through lack of sufficient heavy material in the mixture. Kinetic energy of the mixture is so high and attraction between molecules so small that none of them coalesce to a liquid at stock tank conditions of temperature and pressure.

Testing Fluid Properties and Behavior

As reservoir pressure is reduced and liquid and gas phases are formed, one or the other of the two phases is produced differentially to some degree because of variations of permeability of the rock to gas and oil as fluid saturations change. (See Chapter 2.) Hydrocarbon analysis of the composite production therefore changes from that of the original material in place in the reservoir. Thus, behavior of reservoir fluids during production operations cannot be described completely by what their behavior would be under equilibrium conditions as previously described. Laboratory measurements are needed on phase behavior of reservoir fluid samples for conditions of change where liquid and gas separate both differentially and under equilibrium conditions to solve production problems involving separation under both conditions.

The practical approach to the study of reservoir fluid behavior as practiced by the industry is to anticipate pressure and temperature changes in the reservoir and at the surface during production operations; then measure by laboratory tests the changes occuring to reservoir fluid samples.

Oil Sampling and Testing

Two general methods are used to obtain samples of reservoir oil for laboratory examination purposes—(1) by means of subsurface samplers and (2) by obtaining surface samples of separator liquid and gas. Separator samples of oil and gas are recombined in the laboratory in proportions equivalent to the gas-oil ratio measured at the separator.

Data usually obtained include: (1) original reservoir temperature and pressure; (2) pressure-volume relations at one or more temperatures, one of which is always reservoir temperature (taken as shown in Fig. 45); (3) effects of variation of surface separator pressure on amounts of gas liberated and shrinkage of oil resulting from such separation process; (4) differential gas liberation and oil shrinkage data, taken in the manner shown in Fig. 46; (5) density or specific volume of reservoir fluid; (6) viscosity relation of reservoir oil at reservoir temperature and at pressures ranging from original reservoir pressure to atmospheric pressure and viscosity of stock tank oil; (7) hydrocarbon and orsat analyses of the mixture as it existed originally in the reservoir; and (8) ASTM distillation analyses of residual oil.

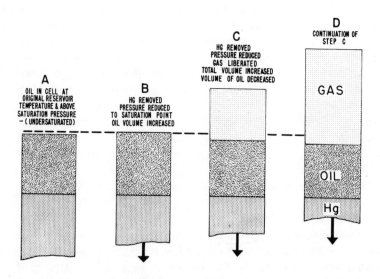

Fig. 45—*Laboratory equilibrium liberation (P-V-T) of gas from oil. (Courtesy* WORLD OIL—*April, 1953.)*

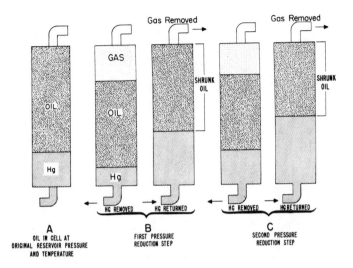

Fig. 46—*Laboratory differential liberation of gas from oil.*
(Courtesy WORLD OIL—*April, 1953.)*

Equilibrium and Differential Data of Oil Samples

If liberated gas is permitted to stay in direct contact with a liquid sample (Fig. 45), a different volume of gas will be liberated down to a given pressure than would be released if the gas were removed from contact with the liquid as it is liberated. The remaining liquid is likewise different in the opposite direction; thus oil shrinkage is different. Differential liberation is that process which takes place when the gas is removed as it is formed incident to a drop in pressure at constant temperature (Fig. 46). Each type of liberation process is encountered to some degree at one time or another in the production of petroleum deposits; therefore, both processes for a given oil sample must be investigated to provide data for a complete reservoir study.

A comparison of equilibrium and differential shrinkage of a low shrinkage oil under reservoir conditions as pressure drops is presented in Fig. 47. This shows that, under equilibrium conditions, a greater quantity of heavy components are progressively pulled into the gas by the light gas components; thus, oil shrinkage is greater. Lower shrinkage by differential liberation under these conditions is caused by gas being removed as it is formed,

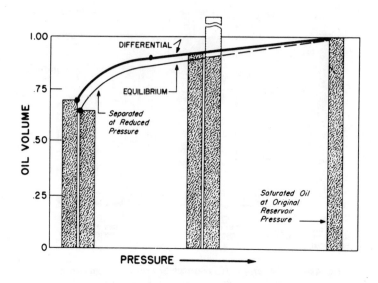

Fig. 47—*Differential and equilibrium shrinkage of low shrinkage oil.*
(Courtesy WORLD OIL—*April, 1953.)*

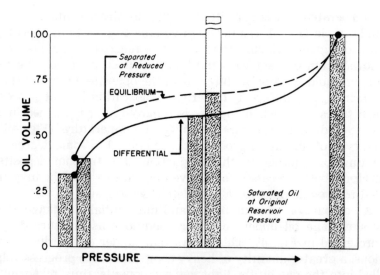

Fig. 48—*Differential and equilibrium shrinkage of high shrinkage oil.*
(Courtesy WORLD OIL—*April, 1953.)*

thereby preventing further attraction of light gas molecules to heavy liquid molecules and minimizing the quantity of liquid pulled into the gas phase.

A comparison between equilibrium and differential shrinkage of a very high shrinkage oil is presented in Fig. 48. In this case, the difference is reversed from that of low shrinkage oil. More gas is formed in the high pressure range than with low shrinkage oil. This is caused by a large quantity of intermediates being pulled into the gas phase (through great attraction to the densely spaced light gas molecules and through high kinetic energy of the intermediates). Once the large quantity of intermediates is removed from the system by differential liberation, they have no further influence on gas liberation and oil shrinkage; therefore, oil shrinkage remains high through lower pressure ranges. If the gas is not removed, as in flash or equilibrium liberation, some intermediate gas molecules may condense because their attraction to light gas molecules is reduced as pressure drops and the light gas molecules become farther apart; thus, vaporizing tendency of high shrinkage oil may be reversed until shrinkage is less under equilibrium conditions than under the differential process.

Shrinkage curves of both low and high shrinkage oil illustrate that, near atmospheric temperature and low pressure conditions, shrinkage of oil greatly increases and presents a problem if maximum liquid volume is to be produced to the stock tank as saleable material.

Oil of all degrees of shrinkage will shrink less to the stock tank if the material is first passed to a separator at some elevated pressure and free gas, formed down to that pressure and temperature, is separated. Also, there is an optimum separator pressure condition where minimum shrinkage of oil is obtained. This will be discussed further in Chapter 10.

Gas Sampling and Testing

Free gas is classified into three general types according to phase behavior upon reduction of temperature or pressure (or both) as illustrated by the phase diagrams in Figs. 42, 43 and 44.

The types are termed retrograde condensate gas, wet gas and dry gas, respectively, and may apply to gas deposits that are either associated or non-associated with oil deposits.

There are two general methods for sampling gas wells. The first utilizes the full-scale field separator and involves recombination of separator material in the laboratory for testing. The second method uses a tubinghead (or line probe) which diverts a portion of produced material to a mobile small-scale separator, portable laboratory or test car which involves performing part of the tests in the field on large samples. Use of the latter method is generally limited to detailed testing of retrograde condensate gas reservoirs.

Information concerning the characteristics and behavior of gas most frequently needed for work with gas reservoirs depends upon the types of gas being considered and the nature of the problem. If the problem at hand involves retrograde condensation as pressure drops, the information needed may become very complex and may require numerous tests and measurements. If the problem involves wet gas (where no retrograde condensation occurs but liquid is recovered in separators) or dry gas (where no liquid is condensed in either the reservoir or separator), then

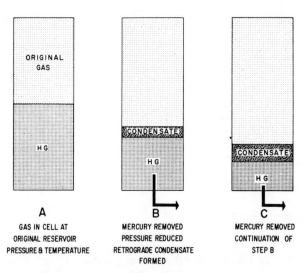

A	B	C
GAS IN CELL AT ORIGINAL RESERVOIR PRESSURE & TEMPERATURE	MERCURY REMOVED PRESSURE REDUCED RETROGRADE CONDENSATE FORMED	MERCURY REMOVED CONTINUATION OF STEP B

Fig. 49—*Equilibrium retrograde condensation of liquid from gas.
(Courtesy* WORLD OIL—*April, 1953.)*

the information needed may be considerably less complex.

Retrograde condensate gas material will be described here. It is important that enough tests be made on gas produced from gas reservoirs to identify the gas positively as to its retrograde characteristics in order for the operator to guard against losing economically recoverable liquids.

Laboratory data of condensate gas reservoir fluids include data on (1) the quantity, hydrocarbon analysis and specific volume of original material in the reservoir, (2) the quantities of vapor and condensed liquid in the reservoir at subsequent reduced reservoir pressures and (3) the complete surface separation history as reservoir pressure decreases, including optimum separation data together with hydrocarbon analyses of separator gas, separator liquid, stock tank gas and stock tank liquid.

Equilibrium and Differential Data of Gas Samples

If pressure is dropped on a gas sample by increasing the volume without withdrawing gas, a different volume of liquid will drop out by retrograde condensation than will occur if pressure is dropped by removing gas without changing the volume of the

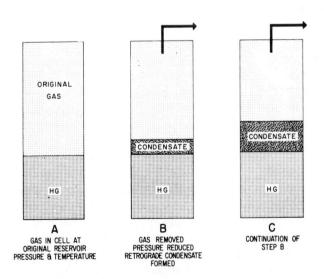

Fig. 50—*Differential retrograde condensation of liquid from gas.*
(Courtesy WORLD OIL—*April, 1953.)*

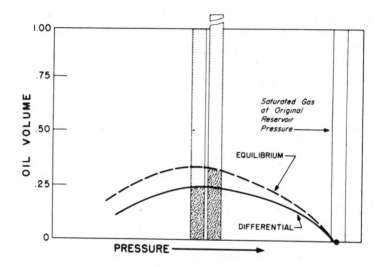

Fig. 51—*Differential and equilibrium condensation of liquid from gas.*
(Courtesy WORLD OIL—*April, 1953.)*

remainder of the sample. The first process, illustrated in Fig. 49,
is termed equilibrium condensation. The latter process, illustrated
in Fig. 50, is termed differential condensation and is analogous to
production from a closed reservoir.

A comparison of equilibrium and differential condensation of
a retrograde gas as measured in the laboratory is presented in
Fig. 51. More liquid condenses under equilibrium conditions than
under differential conditions because a greater quantity of gas
remains in the system in the equilibrium process from which
heavy components may condense as pressure drops.

Condensate Gas Problems

The important problem in condensate gas reservoir material
lies in the change of composition of produced material brought
about by retrograde condensation in the reservoir of the heavier
hydrocarbon components as reservoir pressure drops during production operations. Retrograde condensation characteristics drastically affect desirable operations because it is the condensate
material that provides a large part of the income from the
produced gas. Ultimate loss of income results if liquids are allowed

to condense in the reservoir to form a non-recoverable liquid saturation. Because this liquid saturation is small in per cent of reservoir pore volume, displacement of it from the reservoir other than adajacent to the wellbore may be difficult to accomplish by conventional production of reservoir gas.

The problem of surface separation is involved in the production of gas just as in oil production, whether reservoir conditions at the time of production are at the original or some reduced pressure. It is necessary, therefore, to establish proper separation conditions to recover a maximum amount of liquids in the separator. Obtaining maximum profits from production of gas reservoirs requires solution of these problems. This subject is discussed in detail in Chapter 12.

CHAPTER 4

Distribution of Fluids in the Reservoir

Nearly every oil man has at some time measured the API gravity of oil. Yet in nearly every case, he has had some difficulty in accurately reading the hydrometer used to make this measurement because the oil rises above the level of the sample at the point of contact with the glass stem of the hydrometer. It is little realized that this difficulty in reading the hydrometer results from the same physical characteristic which determines the relative ease with which oil moves in and is produced from tiny pore channels in the reservoir rock. This effect is also responsible for the manner in which gas, oil and water distributions occur in the reservoir rock. The effect is caused by a combination of (1) wettability of the glass to oil and (2) tension in the surface of the oil between oil and air. The curved surface at the edge of the liquid where it contacts the glass surface of the hydrometer stem and which blurs the appearance of the liquid level is called a meniscus.

Wettability

Adhesion is the quality which causes particles of a given material to cling together. If a glass rod is dipped in water and removed, the rod will be wet, showing that some water is more adhesive to glass than to water itself (Fig. 52). The glass rod dipped in mercury will be dry when removed, showing that mercury is more cohesive to itself than adhesive to glass. Water will not adhere to a greasy glass rod, but a clean brass or zinc rod will be wet by either water or mercury because of the adhesion between these materials and the liquids. A liquid, therefore, wets a solid when adhesion of the liquid to the solid is greater than cohesion of liquid particles for each other.

Surface Tension

Surfaces of liquids nearly always are blanketed with what

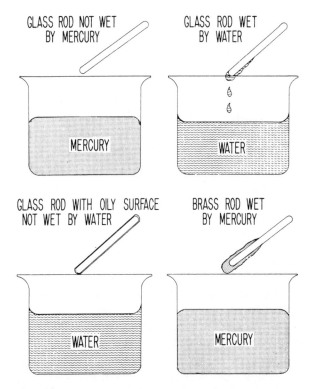

Fig. 52—*Wettability depends on wetting fluid, type of material and condition of surface of material.*

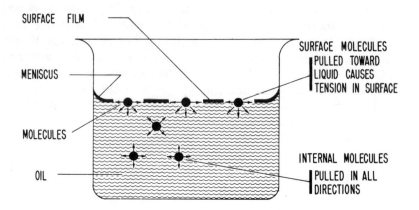

SURFACE FILM

MENISCUS

MOLECULES

OIL

SURFACE MOLECULES PULLED TOWARD LIQUID CAUSES TENSION IN SURFACE

INTERNAL MOLECULES PULLED IN ALL DIRECTIONS

Fig. 53—*Apparent surface film caused by attraction between molecules of liquid.*

acts as a thin film. Although this apparent film possesses little strength, it nevertheless acts like a thin membrane and resists being broken. This is believed to be caused by attraction between molecules within a given material, as shown in Fig. 53. Thus, there exists a tension in the surface of a liquid which is called surface tension. If carefully placed, a needle will float on the surface of water, supported by the film even though considerably more dense than water, and will actually be suspended below the surface by the film.

Capillary Pressure

Some effects of wettability and surface tension are shown in Fig. 54; a drop of water that wets the surface will spread out against tension in the surface film. A drop of mercury that does not wet the surface will be held by surface tension although the mass of the mercury tends to flatten the droplet.

If the open end of a glass capillary tube is inserted into water, the combination of surface tension and wettability of tube to water will cause water to rise in the tube above the water level in the container outside the tube (Fig. 55). If the capillary

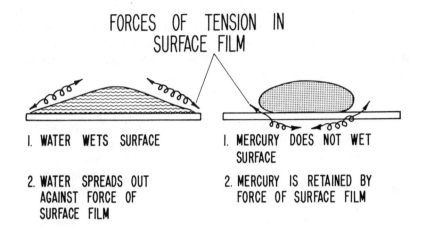

FORCES OF TENSION IN
SURFACE FILM

1. WATER WETS SURFACE

2. WATER SPREADS OUT
AGAINST FORCE OF
SURFACE FILM

1. MERCURY DOES NOT WET
SURFACE

2. MERCURY IS RETAINED BY
FORCE OF SURFACE FILM

Fig. 54—*Effects of wettability and surface tension on action of drops of water and mercury on surface.*

tube is inserted into mercury, lack of wettability of the glass capillary tube to mercury, together with the surface tension of the mercury, will prevent the mercury in the tube from rising even to the fluid level in the container. Size of the capillary tube

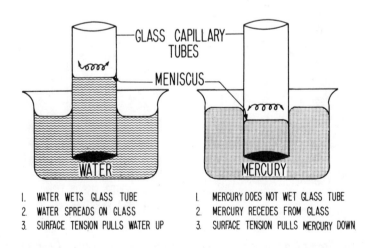

GLASS CAPILLARY
TUBES

MENISCUS

WATER

MERCURY

1. WATER WETS GLASS TUBE
2. WATER SPREADS ON GLASS
3. SURFACE TENSION PULLS WATER UP

1. MERCURY DOES NOT WET GLASS TUBE
2. MERCURY RECEDES FROM GLASS
3. SURFACE TENSION PULLS MERCURY DOWN

Fig. 55—*Rise of water and depression of mercury in glass capillary tube.*

influences the height to which water will rise or the depth to which mercury will depress. Water will rise higher in smaller tubes, as shown in Fig. 56. The same effect occurs in the case of oil; although oil is lighter, it cannot be pulled as high because surface tension in oil is less.

To understand better the reason water rises in a capillary tube, let us further consider the surface tension in the liquid. This film resists being bent just as a plank does. If a plank were placed across two saw horses and a weight suspended from the plank, the plank would bend; if a greater weight were suspended, the plank would bend more. This is similar to what happens when water wets the capillary tube and is pulled up in the tube by liquid wettability and adhesion of the liquid for the tube. At the same time, water forms a weight that pulls the film down in the center of the tube (just as did the weight suspended from the plank).

Material will rise higher in a small tube than a large one because of the difference in amount of pull-down on the film by the weight of water as compared to amount of pull-up by the

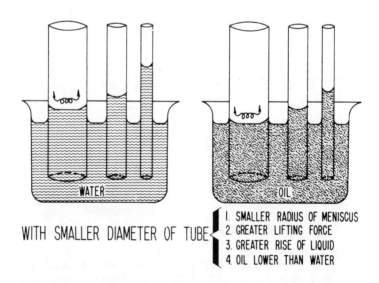

WITH SMALLER DIAMETER OF TUBE
{
1. SMALLER RADIUS OF MENISCUS
2. GREATER LIFTING FORCE
3. GREATER RISE OF LIQUID
4. OIL LOWER THAN WATER

Fig. 56—*Effect of size of capillary tubes on height liquid will be raised in tube.*

wetting action of water to tube. For smaller tubes, the amount of contact of film with glass reduces in proportion to reduction in circumference of the tube. This reduction in contact, and thus pull-up, is not as much as reduction in the volume of water contained by the smaller tube up to a given height. Because the available lift force on the water does not decrease in proportion to the decrease in volume of water it lifts, the force pulls the water higher until it is balanced again at a greater height by total weight of the water. But here another effect occurs. The bending of the film occurs because of the weight of water suspended per unit area of film. The weight of water lifted for a given area is greater in the smaller tube because the water is raised higher. Thus, the liquid is raised higher and the film bent more in the smaller tube.

Visualize the bent film from another standpoint. The film is bent downward because a partial vacuum is created beneath the film by the suspended water (pulling downward on the film) and the surface tension in the film (resisting the downward pull). Pressure is less on the lower (convex) side than on the upper (concave) side of the film. This difference in pressure across the

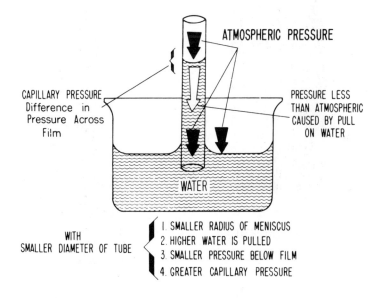

Fig. 57—*Capillary pressure across surface film in capillary tube.*

film is known as capillary pressure (Fig. 57). Capillary forces are, therefore, formed as a result of a combination of wettability and surface tension effects.

Distribution of Fluids

If oil, water and gas were placed in a bottle, the boundary between water and oil would be level; the boundary between oil and gas would be level, with the gas located on top, the oil between and the water below. This distribution would naturally result from the difference in densities of the three materials. If water, oil and gas were placed in the same glass bottle after the bottle had been filled with sand, the distribution of the water, oil and gas would be in the same order (water below, oil between and gas above). However, the contacts between the oil and water and the oil and gas would be quite different from the case where no sand was present. The reason for this is that now the gas, oil

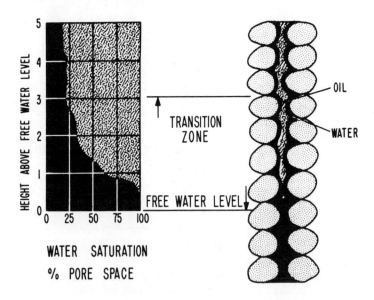

Fig. 58—*Effects of height above free water level on connate-water content in oil sand.*

and water exist in spaces that are capillary in size. Wettability, surface tension and density differences between the three fluids combine to alter the manner in which the fluids occur; the forces present between the fluids in the capillaries caused by these factors are called capillary forces.

In marine sediments, the preferential wetting phase is usually water (probably because of its initial association with water). As oil moved into the sand, water was displaced but left a film along the sand grain surface separating the sand grain from the oil. At any point where the film became broken, contact between the sand grain surface and oil in the absence of water might have allowed the sand at that point to become oil-wet. In the water-wet oil reservoir, some water is held along the sand grain surfaces throughout the reservoir, as illustrated in the enlarged pore channel shown in Fig. 58. Amount of water present in the pores varies from 100 per cent at points below the oil zone of the reservoir to lower and lower percentages at points higher in the oil zone. This is caused by the decreasing radius of the film between oil and water at higher heights. The higher the water is pulled above the 100 per cent water level, the greater the capil-

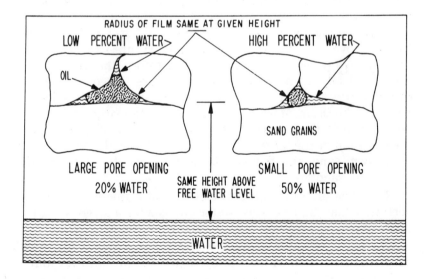

Fig. 59—*Effect of pore size and shape on connate-water content.*

lary film will be bent to suspend the water. As the radius of the bent film becomes smaller, or as the film bend increases due to greater capillary forces, the water fits farther back into the cracks and crevices between sand grains; because of the shape of grains and film, the quantity of water diminishes with reduction in radius of the film at greater heights. The schematic diagram in Fig. 58 shows the change in water saturation with height. Of great importance is the transition zone of saturation of water and oil from a point of 100 per cent water upward in the sand to some point above which water saturation is fairly constant. Theoretically, the amount of water will continue to diminish with height above the free water level; however, it has been found in practice that water saturation becomes fairly constant in uniform sands at points above the transition zone. Therefore, the term "irreducible minimum water saturation" has sometimes been applied to the per cent of water by volume occurring in pore spaces of reservoirs. This water is also referred to as "connate" or "interstitial" water.

It was pointed out earlier that sand grains are irregular, making pore channels between the grains irregular. Sands in different beds or formations differ even more. Other things being equal, pore channels in a lower permeability sand will be smaller; this illustrates an important trend regarding water content of different permeability sands, as shown in Fig. 59. For a given height above the free water level, capillary pressure will be the same in two pores of different size. Therefore, the film between water and oil will have the same curvature for equal pressure; consequently, the amount of water occurring in the crevice will be about the same. More oil is contained in the larger pore space, however, and the per cent of water in the small pore will be greater than in the larger. In general, the lower the permeability of a given sand, the higher will be the connate-water fraction within the sand.

The zone of transition between oil and water will be thicker vertically than that between water and gas for a given texture or permeability of reservoir rock, as shown in Fig. 60. Difference in weight between water and gas is great, and water tends to pull down and seek its own level to a greater extent; however, difference in weight between water and oil is smaller, and water tends to pull down below the oil to a lesser degree. The difference in

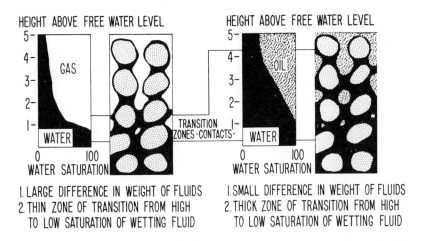

HEIGHT ABOVE FREE WATER LEVEL

1. LARGE DIFFERENCE IN WEIGHT OF FLUIDS
2. THIN ZONE OF TRANSITION FROM HIGH TO LOW SATURATION OF WETTING FLUID

HEIGHT ABOVE FREE WATER LEVEL

1. SMALL DIFFERENCE IN WEIGHT OF FLUIDS
2. THICK ZONE OF TRANSITION FROM HIGH TO LOW SATURATION OF WETTING FLUID

Fig. 60—*Effect of weight of fluids on thickness of transition zones.*

weight between oil and gas is likewise greater than between oil and water; therefore, the transition zone between oil and gas (gas-oil contact) is not so thick as the transition zone between oil and water (water-oil contact).

If permeability of the sand is very low, the zones of transition between water and oil and oil and gas will be spread out more vertically, or be thicker, than those occurring in high permeability sands. This is true because low permeability sands have some smaller pore openings which cause water to be pulled higher above the free water level than would be the case with high permeability sand which has more large pore openings. Therefore, the nature and thickness of the transition zones between water and oil, oil and gas and water and gas are influenced by several factors, among which are the uniformity, permeability and wettability of the rock, and the surface tension and density differences between the fluids involved.

◆

◆

◆

CHAPTER 5

_____

Natural Sources of Energy Available to Produce Oil

What causes oil to flow from a reservoir? This was one of the first fundamental questions that baffled men in the industry. Blowouts, called "gushers", obviously showed that great pressure existed in some oil reservoirs. It was apparent that the presence or absence of pressure inherent within the reservoir had a great deal to do with the ability of a reservoir to give up its oil through the rock pore channels and be produced through the well to the surface. In addition, it was recognized that, when pressure was high, oil was easily produced. When pressure dropped, however, some kind of pumping equipment was needed to help lift the oil to the surface from the bottom of the well. Otherwise, reduced pressure in the reservoir was not sufficient to move the oil beyond some point within the well. Recognition of the part reservoir pressure played in oil production and the need to produce a maximum amount of oil before pressure dissipated was one of the greatest developments of the science of producing reservoirs.

The energy available in nature to produce petroleum deposits had its origin in the same environment in which petroleum originated. As layer upon layer of sediments were laid down, the pore spaces were full of the water in which sediments were deposited. Burial beneath hundreds or thousands of feet of sediments created pressure which compacted the rocks. If the pore channels are inter-connected through all the sediments to the sea or the surface of the land, pressure existing within the fluids in the rock is the pressure exerted by the weight of that fluid and is independent of the weight of the rock. Pressure in the fluid within a given porous rock will normally be about 46 pounds per square inch per 100 feet of depth—the amount of pressure exerted by a column of salt water. Pressure in a reservoir 1,000-feet deep will then be about 460 pounds per square inch. Weight of the rock overburden is supported principally by the rock itself because less pressure occurs in the fluid than is required to support the rock overburden. Rock porosity is not influenced to a great extent by rock overburden; however, at great depths porosity is thought to diminish because of great rock overburden pressures. This occurs even in rock which probably had high porosity while existing at shallower depths before earth crustal movements displaced it to greater depths.

Where the pore space in some portions of sediments are isolated or have no continuity to sea or land surfaces, pressure within the fluid in the pore spaces may be lower or higher than if there were continuous pore channels connected to sea or land surfaces. The continuous processes of the earth's crust — raising, lowering, grain compaction and grain cementation—cause variations in pressure within the pore spaces. When sediments deep in the earth rise to shallower depths, they may trap and retain abnormally high pressures. The pressure would be lowered to normal, however, if the fluids were connected through continuous pore channels to sea or land surfaces.

Hydrocarbon compounds making up petroleum were formed and accumulated in the enviroment of varying degrees of pressure which, being submerged in water, was always greater than atmospheric pressure. Pressures greater than 10,000 pounds per square inch have been found at great depths, and reservoirs in which even much greater pressures occur will probably be discovered as still greater depths are reached.

Reservoir Drives

Although it has long been recognized that pressure drives oil to the wellbore, this fact alone was not sufficient to explain the way oil is produced and the reasons for the many peculiar production problems that confront the oil producer.

In an oil reservoir, generally a very complex set of circumstances causes oil to flow through pore channels to the wellbore and be produced. As production starts, pressure drops in the oil adjacent to the wellbore. This pressure drop drains oil from out in the reservoir toward the point of oil withdrawal. Oil, connate water and the rock itself are all under compression and occupy less space at high pressure than they do at low pressure. With oil withdrawal, pressure drops in the reservoir and the oil, water and rock expand. Expansion of all these materials has an influence on oil production; however, the combined influence is responsible for production of only a relatively small part of oil initially in a reservoir.

Most of the oil is driven to the wells in natural production through expansion of free gas from within or water from outside the reservoir. Gas to furnish energy to displace oil to the wells comes from two sources — gas dissolved in the oil at high pressure and liberated as reservoir pressure drops, and gas free at original reservoir conditions and in the sand above the oil as a gas cap. Water that furnishes energy to displace oil to the wells comes from outside the oil zone or from the water leg, or "aquifer", that occurs in contiguous sand beyond the extremities of the oil zone.

In an oil reservoir, production results from a mechanism which utilizes existing pressure. This is the drive mechanism. The reservoir having a recovery mechanism that uses principally the liberation and expansion of dissolved gas is termed a "dissolved gas drive reservoir"; one that uses principally the expansion of a cap of free gas over the oil zone is termed a "gas cap drive reservoir"; and one that uses principally influx and movement of water from outside the reservoir is termed a "water drive reservoir".

Dissolved Gas Drive

Many oil deposits are found in porous rock, either sandstone or limestone, with the porous area of the formation in which the oil is contained completely surrounded by dense non-permeable rock (Fig. 61). Such deposits immediately present evidence against distant migration in the accumulation process. This could be the result of oil exchange from a shale source bed with original water from an adjacent sandstone bed by capillary pressure forces. Such forces are ever present in porous rocks when two non-mixable, or "immiscible", fluids such as water and oil occur together. An oil deposit of this nature can be thought of as being in a container of a fixed volume completely filled with oil except for the "connate" water that occurs as a microscopic film on the sand grains.

A reservoir of this physical nature inevitably becomes a dissolved gas drive type of reservoir when produced. This name is

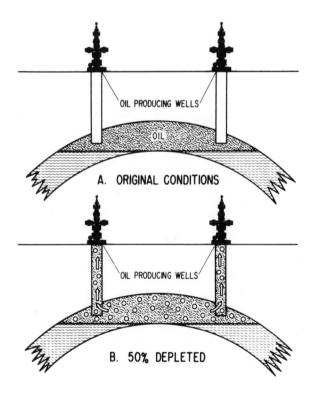

Fig. 61—*Dissolved gas drive reservoir.*

not taken from the shape or condition of the reservoir but from the source of energy which produces the oil. This energy is derived from the light hydrocarbons in solution in the hydrocarbon liquid mixture in the reservoir. These light hydrocarbons are liberated from solution as oil is produced and reservoir pressure drops, forming a gas phase as contrasted to the liquid phase in which the rest of the reservoir hydrocarbon materials remain. Being highly expansible, the gas furnishes energy to push oil to the wellbore as pressure continues to decline. Notable examples of reservoirs having dissolved gas drive at discovery are the Canyon Reef Trend fields in Scurry County, Tex.; Comodoro Rivadavia field, Argentina; Agua Grande field, Bahia, Brazil; Belayim field, Egypt; and Joffre field, Canada.

Dissolved gas drive reservoirs behave characteristically during their producing life. These behavior patterns pertain to changes in oil production rates, pressure and ratios of gas and oil produced during the life of the reservoir.

After a well is drilled into a dissolved gas drive-type reservoir and production commences, pressure drops in the vicinity of the point where the well penetrated the reservoir. This pressure drop at the well causes fluids to expand from out in the reservoir, driving oil through the tiny pore channels to the well. Pressure in reservoir fluids declines because of the oil withdrawal. Gas evolves from solution and occurs as small separate bubbles in individual pore spaces, occupying space vacated by withdrawal of the oil. At first, bubbles of gas formed by liberation from liquid solution of the light components do not move because the round bubbles lodge in the small openings between pore spaces. As oil withdrawal continues, further pressure decline takes place and more and more free gas is formed. This increases the size of individual bubbles until they enlarge sufficiently to join in a continuous thread of gas through pore channels. The gas thus formed in a thread-like state begins to flow (Fig. 31).

Gas flows more easily than oil because it is lighter, less viscous and does not cling to the surfaces of the pore spaces in the rock. Once gas commences to flow, a chain reaction seems to take place; pressure drops faster and lets greater amounts of gas be formed from light hydrocarbons in the liquid. With small additional amounts of oil produced from the reservoir, small additional increases in gas space are created. Gas thus flows much more easily while oil flows with greatly increasing difficulty. "Gas-oil ratio", or volume of gas flowing compared to volume of oil flowing, increases until pressure reaches such a low point that both oil and gas flow ceases. Because of a depletion in pressure or energy, most oil in the last stages of production must be lifted by pumps from the well, the energy available being sufficient to push the oil to the well but not enough to lift it to the surface. Oil is more difficult to move to the well, and the production rate diminishes during the latter portion of the producing life of the reservoir. The measured producing gas-oil ratio at surface conditions, in cubic feet of gas per barrel of oil in the stock tank, changes throughout the producing life of the reservoir. At first, because some gas liberated from the produced oil is held by tiny restrictions in the pore channels, produced ratio is less than the ratio of the gas originally dissolved in the oil in the reservoir. The produced gas-oil ratio increases when gas in the pore channels becomes long continuous threads of free gas and starts to flow from the reservoir. It continues to increase until some low reservoir pressure condition is reached. When this happens the measured ratio at the surface may diminish because, at lower pressures, the volumes of gas in the reservoir become more nearly equal to the volumes measured at the surface.

Little or no water is ever produced from a dissolved gas drive reservoir because of the very nature of the reservoir; it is a closed trap filled with oil and non-producible connate water.

Recovery of oil from a dissolved gas drive reservoir by its own energy is nearly always very low — 5 to 30 per cent of original oil being a range of ultimate recoveries encompassing nearly all dissolved gas drive reservoirs. Fig. 62 and Table 1 summarize these characteristic trends occuring during production life of dissolved gas drive reservoirs.

The low recovery from dissolved gas drive reservoirs em-

TABLE 1—DISSOLVED GAS DRIVE RESERVOIRS

Characteristics	Trend
1. Reservoir pressure	Declines rapidly and continuously
2. Surface gas-oil ratio	First low, then rises to maximum and then drops
3. Water production	None
4. Well behavior	Requires pumping at early stage
5. Expected oil recovery	5 to 30 per cent of original oil in place

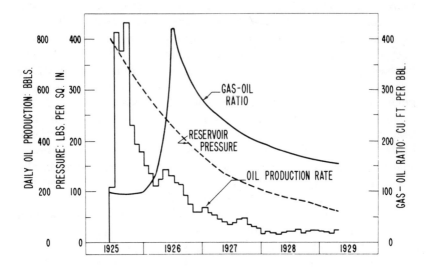

Fig. 62—*Production data—dissolved gas drive reservoir. (Courtesy* API, Drilling and Production Practices—*1943.)*

phasizes that large quantities of oil remain in the reservoir rocks after they are abandoned. Under such conditions, these reservoirs are voided of their small amount of inherent energy to produce their own oil. To obtain greater recoveries from this type reservoir, energy must be applied from some man-made source. It is to this type reservoir, therefore, that the petroleum industry turns first to add to its future recoverable reserves as the science of oil production develops new and more efficient ways to recover the maximum amount of oil from reservoir rocks.

Gas Cap Drive

On many occasions, oil accumulations occurred in which there were greater volumes of light materials present than would dissolve in the oil at temperature and pressure conditions existing in the reservoir. Stated another way, pressure was not great enough to retain all the light materials in liquid form. When this occurred, the light materials with some intermediate and

heavy components formed a free gas phase. This free gas bub-
bled up to the top of the deposit where it was trapped and
formed a cap of gas over the oil. This excess gas in its compressed state then became a source of energy to move oil to the
wellbore and lift it to the surface. If a reservoir of this nature
occurs in an isolated volume of rock porosity with dense rock
surrounding the reservoir, the natural energy available to produce the oil comes from two sources — the expansion of the gas-
cap gas and expansion of the dissolved gas as it is liberated (both
occurring with pressure drop caused by oil production). A reservoir of this nature is termed a gas cap drive reservoir (Fig. 63).
Some reservoirs producing by gas cap drive are the Hawkins
field, Wood County, Tex., and the Aga Jari field, Iran.

In the gas cap drive mechanism, oil level in the reservoir falls

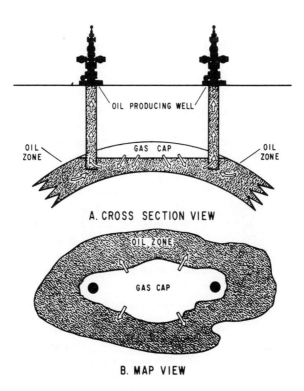

Fig. 63—*Gas cap drive reservoir.*

as production proceeds, the gas cap expanding down into the section of the reservoir originally containing oil. Pressure tends to be maintained at a higher level than in a dissolved gas drive reservoir. This of course depends upon volume of gas in the gas cap compared to oil volume. The larger the volume of the gas cap, the less the pressure will drop as oil is produced from beneath the cap. This maintenance of pressure on the oil accomplishes several benefits. Dissolved gas is held in solution within the oil itself. The oil is thus lighter and less viscous and will move more easily toward the wells. A driving action of the expanding gas cap pushes oil down-structure ahead of the expanding gas cap, sustaining the production rates of the wells. Gas-oil ratios, however, may rise in wells that are overtaken by the moving gas-cap front. Water production is not a characteristic of a gas cap drive reservoir because such a reservoir does not enclose water except for connate water that may occur as a microscopic film on the sand grains. Because of effects of gas-cap expansion on maintaining reservoir pressure and effect of decreased liquid column weight as it is produced out the well, gas cap drive reservoirs tend to flow longer than dissolved gas drive reservoirs depending, of course, upon quantity of gas in the gas cap and pressure in the reservoir. Recovery to be expected from such a reservoir will depend upon many things. Size of the gas cap, however, a measure of reservoir energy available to produce the oil, will in large part determine recovery per cent to be expected. Such recovery normally will be 20 to 40 per cent of original oil in place; but if some other features are present to assist such as steep angle of dip which allows good oil drainage to the bottom of the structure, considerably higher recoveries (up to 60 per cent or greater) may be obtained. Conversely, extremely thin oil columns (where early breakthrough of the advancing gas cap occurs in producing wells) may limit oil recovery to lower figures regardless of cap

TABLE 2—GAS CAP DRIVE RESERVOIRS

Characteristics	Trend
1. Reservoir pressure	Falls slowly and continuously
2. Surface gas-oil ratio	Rises continuously in up-structure wells
3. Water production	Absent or negligible
4. Well behavior	Long flowing life depending upon size of gas cap
5. Expected oil recovery	20 to 40 per cent

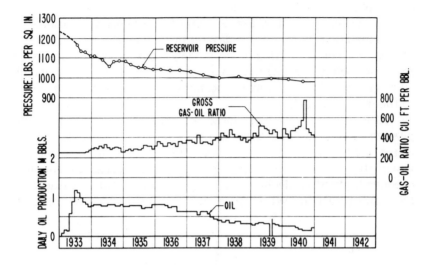

Fig. 64—*Production data—gas cap drive reservoir. (Courtesy* API, DRILLING AND PRODUCTION PRACTICES—*1943.)*

size since the entire well stream consists of material originally contained in the gas cap. Fig. 64 and Table 2 summarize characteristic trends occurring during the producing life of gas cap drive reservoirs.

In gas cap drive reservoirs, a large proportion of original oil is trapped and retained following the natural producing life of such a reservoir. After abandonment, this type reservoir does not have the great amount of oil left in the rock that is present in the dissolved gas drive reservoir at its depleted abandonment conditions; however, large quantities of oil left behind can provide future reserves when proper recovery methods are devised.

Water Drive

The greatest natural source of energy available to produce oil today traces its source back to the ancient seas in which the present-day rock formations were formed as sedimentary deposits, the same ancient seas in which present-day oil deposits originated as organic substances. This source of energy is the great quantity of salt water existing in the porous channels of rock associated with present-day oil deposits. One must visualize the rock layer occurring over a very large area, with the oil reservoir being a relatively small structural feature into which oil migrated. Therefore, water occurs over a large area compared to the oil in the rock.

Although water is considered incompressible, the total compressed volume is quite large when such great quantities of total water volume are involved. Even the great volume of rock in which the water exists is influenced by water pressure. As oil is produced, pressure declines at the point where oil is withdrawn from the reservoir. Water then moves in to replace the oil as it

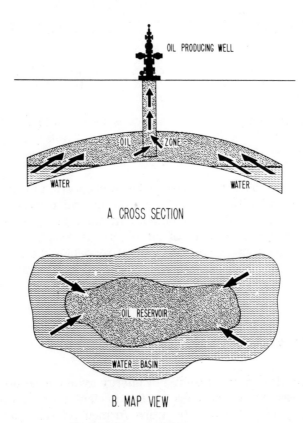

Fig. 65—*Water drive reservoir.*

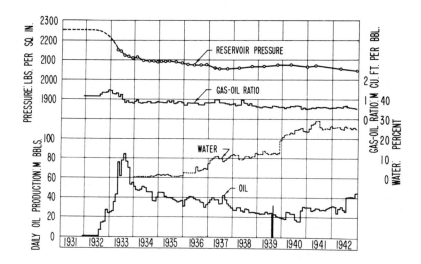

Fig. 66—*Production data— water drive reservoir. (Courtesy* API,
DRILLING AND PRODUCTION PRACTICES—*1943.)*

is produced because of expansion of the minutely compressed
water; a reservoir producing in this manner is termed a "water
drive reservoir" (Fig. 65). Many of the most important reservoirs

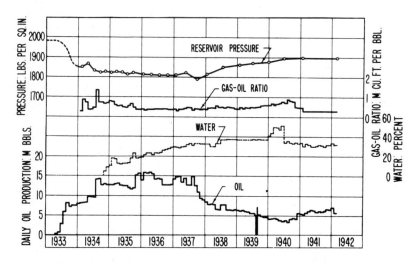

Fig. 67—*Effect of production rate on pressure in a water drive reservoir.*
(Courtesy API, DRILLING AND PRODUCTION PRACTICES—*1943.)*

in the world are producing by energy supplied by water drives. Notable examples are the East Texas field; Leduc field, Alberta, Canada; Burgan field, Kuwait; Gela field, Sicily; and the Wafra field, Neutral Zone, Arabia.

The gas-oil ratio remains about the same in a water drive reservoir because pressure, remaining high, prevents gas from evolving to form a high gas saturation. Water production begins first in wells completed low on the structure because the water, in its displacing action on oil, arrives at these wells first. Water production in these wells increases continuously until the wells must be abandoned because oil production is insufficient to economically justify their continued operation (Fig. 66). A much larger portion of oil originally in the reservoir is produced by energy and action of a water drive than by either dissolved gas drive or gas cap drive. Such recovery normally will be approximately 35 to 75 per cent of original oil in place.

Fig. 66 and Table 3 summarize the characteristic trends occurring during the producing life of water drive reservoirs.

Water drive has an important difference from other types of reservoir drives — the degree to which reservoir pressure is maintained in a water drive reservoir depends upon the relation between rate of oil, gas and water production and rate at which the water can advance through the sands into the reservoir. At low rates of production, reservoir pressure remains nearly as high as pressure in the oil when discovered. At fast rates of production, the reservoir pressure is pulled down. When the rate is once again reduced, however, pressure will increase (Fig. 67).

It is common to speak of edge water or bottom water in discussing water influx into a reservoir. Bottom water occurs directly beneath the oil and edge water occurs off the flanks of the structure at the edge of the oil. Regardless of the source of water, the water drive is the result of water moving into the pore spaces

TABLE 3—WATER DRIVE RESERVOIRS

Characteristics	Trend
1. Reservoir pressure	Remains high
2. Surface gas-oil ratio	Remains low
3. Water production	Starts early and increases to appreciable amounts
4. Well behavior	Flow until water production gets excessive
5. Expected oil recovery	35 to 75 per cent

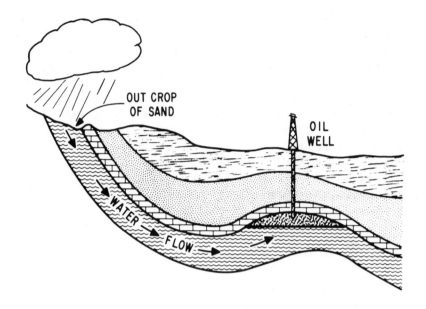

Fig. 68—*Reservoir having artesian water drive.*

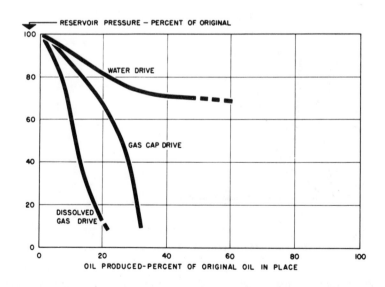

Fig. 69—*Reservoir pressure trends for reservoirs under various drives.
(Courtesy* API, DRILLING AND PRODUCTION PRACTICES—*1943.)*

originally occupied by oil, replacing the oil and driving it to the producing wells. Water drive may come about as a result of artesian flow from an outcrop of the formation in which the reservoir occurs at some short distance from the reservoir. Surface water is gathered at the outcrop and feeds down into the formation, replenishing the water as it moves into the reservoir to replace the produced oil (Fig. 68). This type of water drive is not often encountered, particularly during the early producing life of the reservoir.

Graphical comparison of the changes in pressures and gas-oil ratios during the producing life of reservoirs of the three basic drives is generalized in Figs. 69 and 70.

Combination Drive

Reservoirs of oil can be typed according to their geological configuration or according to their producing mechanism, but

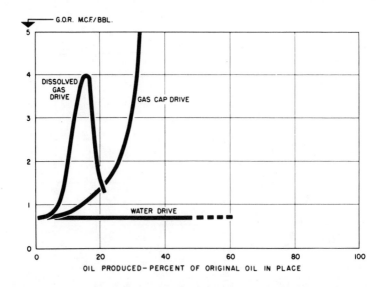

Fig. 70—*Reservoir gas-oil ratio trends for reservoirs under various drives. (Courtesy* API, DRILLING AND PRODUCTION PRACTICES—*1943.)*

reservoirs are seldom found which can be made to fit exactly into either type of classification. The producing mechanism most commonly encountered is one in which both water and free gas are available in some degree to enter the reservoir and displace the oil toward the wells as production occurs (Fig. 71). The most common type of drive encountered, therefore, is a combination drive. Production problems are exceedingly complicated because of the infinite number of combinations characterizing the various reservoirs occurring naturally.

Differences between the three basic drive mechanisms resolve into those which occur between a depletion and a displacement mechanism. The depletion mechanism applies where energy

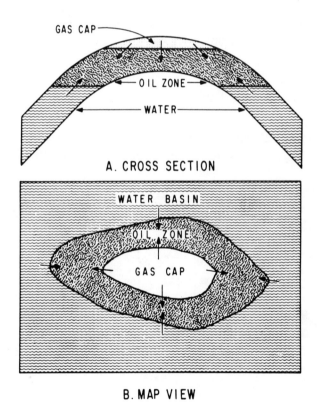

Fig. 71—*Combination drive reservoir.*

comes principally from the small amount of gas originally dissolved in the reservoir oil. Only by exhausting this supply of gas through liberation, expansion and depletion is oil produced. The displacement mechanism applies to both gas cap and water drives where either gas or water as the displacing material originates outside the oil zone, moves into the oil zone through the interconnecting pore channels and pushes oil ahead to the wellbore. The depletion mechanism is inherently inefficient because large percentages of oil are left in such reservoirs that depend on dissolved gas for their driving energy. Although large amounts of oil are left behind in most reservoirs having a displacement-type drive (gas cap or water drive), such drives are inherently more efficient. The first great task facing the oil industry, therefore, is to minimize the inefficient drives by substituting more efficient ones to obtain better recoveries from known petroleum deposits.

Gravitational Segregation

Gravitational segregation, or gravity drainage, may be placed in a class by itself as a driving mechanism; however, it is con-

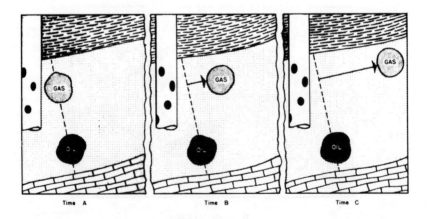

Fig. 72—*Gravitational segregation showing relative movement of gas and oil along the structure at various times during non-producing periods. (Courtesy* WORLD OIL—*June, 1951.)*

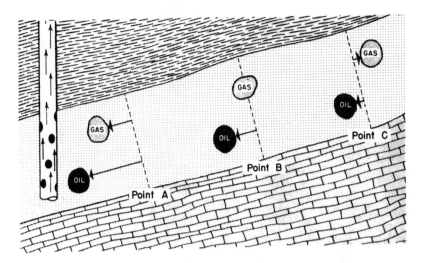

Fig. 73—*Gravitational segregation showing relative movement of gas and oil along the structure at various distances from a producing well.*
(Courtesy WORLD OIL—*June, 1951.)*

sidered rather as a modification of all types of drives. Gravitational segregation is the tendency (due to the forces of gravity) for gas, oil and water to return to a distribution in the reservoir according to their densities after the reservoir has been produced and the natural arrangement of the fluids has been disturbed. Gravity drainage can play a great part in recovery of oil from a reservoir. For example, if conditions are suitable recovery from some dissolved gas drive reservoirs may be increased to that of good water drive reservoirs by gravity drainage. Other reservoirs may have (by proper control of producing rates) their gravity drainage effects increased to provide a definite increase in oil recovery. Fig. 72 illustrates the relative movement of gas to oil in the reservoir at different times by gravitational segregation under reservoir conditions of non-production following periods of production. Fig. 73 illustrates that at a given time the relative movement of gas to oil at various points in the reservoir is approximately the same, although within a certain radius of the well (depending upon the rate of production) both gas and oil are moving toward the well because of the high pressure gradients existing near the well.

◆

◆

◆

CHAPTER 6

Producing Characteristics
Of Oil Wells

Close examination of the three basic types of reservoir drives is revealing and helpful in classifying fundamental well production characteristics. Pressure, gas production and water production trends are producing characteristics of oil wells of particular significance. Although these problems are not the only ones encountered in production operations (others are sanding conditions, paraffin deposition, equipment problems, etc.), this book will discuss only problems induced by reservoir flow performance.

Each of the three basic reservoir drive mechanisms inherently causes well production problems. The limited amount of available reservoir energy in a dissolved gas drive reservoir controls the length of time a well may flow. In a gas cap drive reservoir the advance of the expanding gas cap eventually reaches the oilwell completion interval, resulting in ever increasing gas-oil ratios which limit the further production of oil. In a water drive reservoir water advances as the oil ahead is produced, leading to water production along with the oil. Continued water advance is accompanied by increasing water-oil ratios until economic limits of production are reached, first for the wells low on the structure and later for all wells in the reservoir.

Pressure Trends

As tubing pressure of a well falls, the pumper will begin to keep closer watch on the well and adjust the choke size in an attempt to continue to produce the desired daily amount of oil. When pressure falls too much, production may decline and the well may flow by heads—then eventually cease flowing entirely. In some cases it may be put back on production by swabbing, although frequent swabbing and other well work is expensive, and causes economic problems as costs begin to rise and production falls off. Problems may be solved in some cases by additional costly re-conditioning or in others by installation of lift equipment, but these procedures require further expenditures.

Oil has little natural ability to produce itself into a wellbore. It is produced principally by pressure inherent in gas dissolved

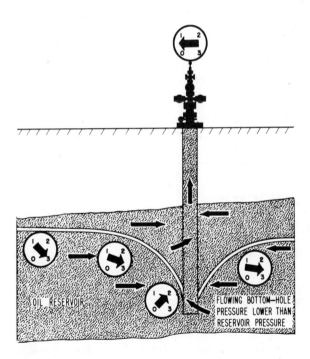

Fig. 74—*Pressure conditions around a flowing well.*

in oil or from associated free gas caps or from associated salt water basins.

Just how pressure is distributed throughout the reservoir and what causes it to change is of great significance in interpreting well production trends caused by pressure characteristics. Fig. 74 shows a schematic cross-section in an oil reservoir through a producing well. Out in the reservoir away from the well, pressure is about 3,000 pounds; at a point nearer the well, pressure decreases to about 2,700 pounds. Within the casing opposite the completion interval, pressure is 2,000 pounds; and at the wellhead, pressure is down to about 600 pounds. This large decrease in pressure from bottom-hole to tubing-head is caused by hydraulic pressure drop in the fluid column in the tubing and the drop in pressure caused by friction of flow in the tubing. In the background of the illustration is a curved "ghost" line indicating the manner in which the pressure changes from point to point in the reservoir.

Most of the 1,000-pound pressure drop in the reservoir occurs fairly close to the wellbore. In a completely uniform sand, the pressure drop across the last 15 feet of the formation surrounding the wellbore is about one-half of the total pressure drop from the well to a point 500-feet away in the reservoir (Fig. 75). The

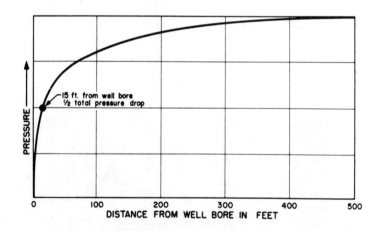

Fig. 75—*Pressure drop within 15-foot radius of flowing wellbore is about one-half the total pressure drop measured from a 500-foot radius of the wellbore. (Courtesy* THE PETROLEUM ENGINEER—*Sept., 1956.)*

reason for this concentrated area of pressure drop is that fluids flowing in from a large drainage area of 40 acres, for example, are funneled through a bottleneck as they come into the completion zone — much as automobile traffic stacks up and funnels through a busy intersection.

Because fluids move toward the well from all directions, the term "radial flow" is given to flow of fluid into a wellbore. Pressure distribution around the well is sometimes called a "pressure sink" since wellbore pressure has sunk below that of the surrounding formation. In order to have a high tubing pressure, reservoir pressure must be sufficient to offset both hydraulic pressure drop in the fluid column in the tubing and pressure drop in the pressure sink — then still have the necessary pressure level available at the tubing head to permit the well to flow to the stock tanks at the desired rate of production. Where reservoir rock characteristics and fluid saturations are uniform throughout the reservoir, the pressure sink will be categorically a uniform one; however, if they vary from the wellbore to the outlying reservoir, the pressure sink will be distorted through the zones of varying rock characteristics and fluid distribution.

In reservoirs with uniform sand and fluid conditions, two factors may cause low flowing bottom-hole pressures in the wells. These are permeability of the sand and producing rate (Fig. 76). With a high permeability sand or restricted rate of production, bottom-hole flowing pressure will be relatively high since these conditions result in moderate pressure drawdowns (Fig. 76A). With low permeability sand or excessive rate of production, the pressure drawdown will be appreciably higher — thus reducing flowing bottom-hole pressures and possibly requiring that the wells be put on artificial lift if high rates are desired (Fig. 76B).

Low flowing bottom-hole pressure many times occurs through damage to permeability adjacent to the wellbore caused by drilling or producing operations themselves. This is unfortunate because at this point in the reservoir restriction is greatly magnified in effect. This abnormal permeability condition is termed "skin effect". Fig. 77 shows (A) a normal pressure sink compared to (B) a pressure sink in a well where the formation has been damaged.

The skin effect may result from any of a number of causes such as clay swelling from contact with fresh water filtrate from

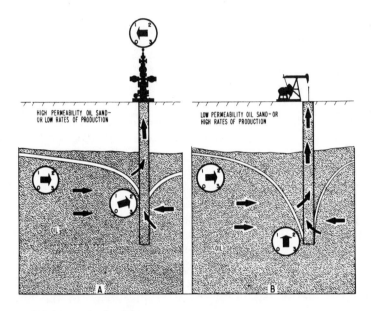

Fig. 76—*Effects of permeability and production rates on bottom-hole and tubing-head pressures.*

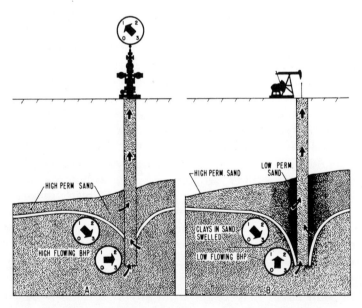

Fig. 77—*Influence of skin effect on pressure around a wellbore.*

drilling muds, mud cake penetrating into and sticking to the formation wall in the well, bit glazing of the wellbore, water blocking of the pore channels adjacent to the wellbore, etc. (Fig. 78).

So many individual or combinations of conditions cause a skin effect that it is somewhat difficult, if not impossible, in most cases to interpret what is causing the permeability block. Solving it usually requires some trial-and-error use of various methods of well stimulation. Ordinarily if the reduction in permeability causing the skin effect can be identified, treatment to restore permeability can be effected. Such treatment may be performed with surface tension breakers, acids, hydraulic fracturing or a combination of treating materials or methods.

For many decades stimulation of wells completed in very low

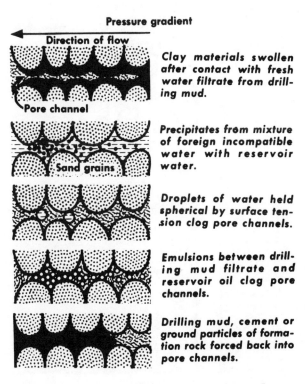

Pressure gradient

Direction of flow

Pore channel

Clay materials swollen after contact with fresh water filtrate from drilling mud.

Sand grains

Precipitates from mixture of foreign incompatible water with reservoir water.

Droplets of water held spherical by surface tension clog pore channels.

Emulsions between drilling mud filtrate and reservoir oil clog pore channels.

Drilling mud, cement or ground particles of formation rock forced back into pore channels.

Fig. 78—*Reservoir conditions causing skin effect.* (*Courtesy* THE PETROLEUM ENGINEER—*Sept. 1956.*)

Well Bore

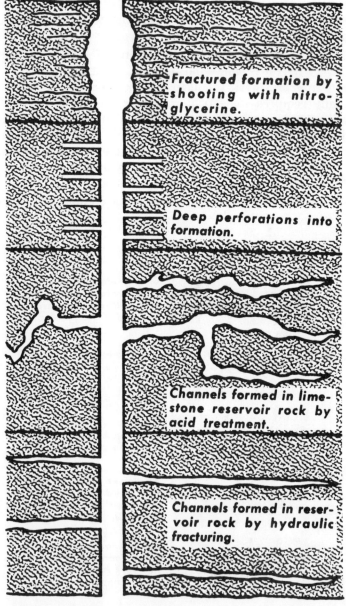

Fractured formation by shooting with nitro-glycerine.

Deep perforations into formation.

Channels formed in lime-stone reservoir rock by acid treatment.

Channels formed in reservoir rock by hydraulic fracturing.

Fig. 79—*Well stimulation in low permeability reservoirs. (Courtesy* THE PETROLEUM ENGINEER—*Sept. 1956.)*

permeability formations has been practiced to increase drastically permeability in the volume of reservoir rock extending some distance out from the wellbore. These stimulation practices include shooting with nitroglycerin, deep perforating, acidizing, and more recently, by hydraulic fracturing with oil, acids and other fluids (Fig. 79).

The basic characteristic of the reservoir drive or course has a direct bearing on whether or not bottom-hole pressures will be maintained to a high level by natural reservoir energy.

In the case of the dissolved gas drive reservoir, pressure will soon be depleted with continued production. In the case of the water drive reservoir, water production will make the fluid column in the tubing heavier and reduce surface tubing pressure to the extent that artificial lift may be required even though reservoir pressure is being maintained at a high level by continued water influx (Fig. 80A).

The oil well in a gas cap drive reservoir completed near the gas cap will be invaded as the gas cap expands, will begin to produce free gas, and the gas will make the fluid column in the

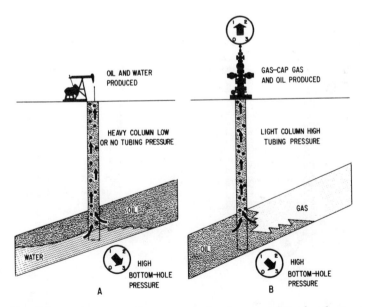

Fig. 80—*Effects of water and gas-cap production on tubing-head pressure.*

tubing lighter. This results in a higher wellhead tubing pressure which appears to relieve the operator of well production problems of lifting the oil. Even bottom-hole pressure seems to be maintained somewhat by expansibility of the gas cap, provided withdrawal rates are not excessive (Fig. 80B). This is all somewhat paradoxical, however, because production of free gas from the gas cap, not contributing toward the displacement of the oil, is a waste of natural reservoir energy for oil production and may reduce energy in the gas cap by reducing gas-cap pressure and possibly even permitting the gas cap to shrink (Fig. 81A). Under these conditions, an offending well can cause all other wells in the oil column to go on artificial lift as gas-cap pressure is wasted and oil zone pressure reduced. Elimination of free gas production through the up-dip wells as the gas cap expands tends to conserve and maintain native reservoir energy and allow the down-dip oil wells to flow longer (Fig. 81B).

Possibility of blowouts, casing leaks or channeling leaks is always present, providing hazardous loss of reservoir pressure. Fig. 82 shows conditions (A) before and (B) after a casing leak

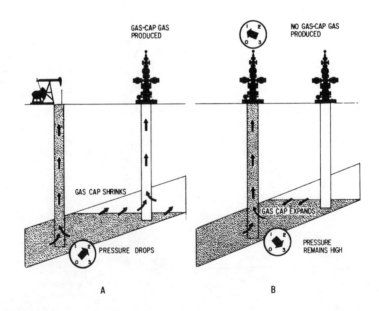

Fig. 81—*Effects of gas-cap gas production on reservoir pressure.*

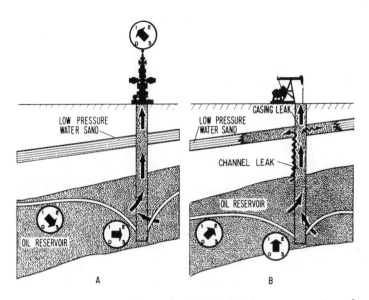

Fig. 82—*Effects of casing and channel leaks on reservoir and tubing pressure.*

and a channeling leak have developed along the casing permitting loss of reservoir fluids into a shallow low pressure water sand. A casing leak can be more detrimental than a channeling leak because it is more likely to occur some distance up the hole where pressure differential is large and fluid flow between productive and shallow sand is much greater. Casing leaks, however, are usually easier to detect and repair. Leaks are usually first recognized by abrupt changes in reservoir conditions such as rapid pressure drop in a given well where the leak occurs or production of water or free gas in wells adjacent to the problem well.

If the natural reservoir drive is limited in energy, reservoir pressure will fall rapidly and artificial lift will be required (Fig. 83A). It may, however, be profitable from the standpoint of increasing recovery to augment the natural drive, in some cases even at considerable investment and operating expense. This is frequently accomplished by injecting either gas or water into the reservoir for pressure maintenance.

Fluid injection programs for pressure maintenance are usually designed not only to sustain reservoir pressure at levels which provide increased flowing life to wells but also to increase ultimate recovery from the reservoir.

A gas injection pressure maintenance program is usually operated much like a naturally occuring gas cap drive, i.e., injection into structurally high wells to induce a gas cap. Well performance may be expected to follow the same trends as in natural gas cap drive reservoirs, increasing gas-oil ratios and flowing well performance to economic limit. Incentives for installing such a program lie in the increased oil recovery which may be effected and in savings in operating expenses, such as foregoing the purchase and maintenance of artificial lift equipment.

Water injection pressure maintenance operations are quite often designed to approximate naturally occuring water drive for the reservoir. Water is usually injected down structure or possibly in the aquifer itself. Again flowing life is extended until the water-cut in producing wells becomes high and gas-oil ratios remain constant. Increased oil recovery provides the economic basis for the installation of such a program.

Gas Production Trends

Production of gas from an oil producing well comes from either or both the gas originally dissolved in the reservoir oil at high pressures and the free gas that has, during geologic time, segregated and become trapped above the oil as a gas cap (Fig. 84). Free gas production may also come through channels in bad cement jobs or casing leaks from a high pressure gas reservoir entirely separate from the oil reservoir (Fig. 85).

In reservoirs that exhibit dissolved gas drive characteristics, some gas in the oil at original pressure is liberated from solution as oil production occurs and reservoir pressure drops. Continued liberation and expansion of free gas is a characteristic, although an inefficient one, for primary oil recovery from a reservoir of this type. Increase in gas saturation, however, as oil withdrawals continue, permits gas to flow toward low-pressure areas at the wellbores and be produced along with oil and its still dissolved gas. This gas is free and flowing in the reservoir although it had earlier been in solution in the oil. After production proceeds to a

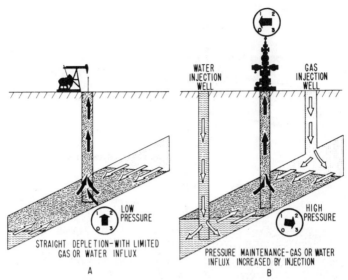

Fig. 83—*Effects of gas or water pressure maintenance on the producing ability of wells.*

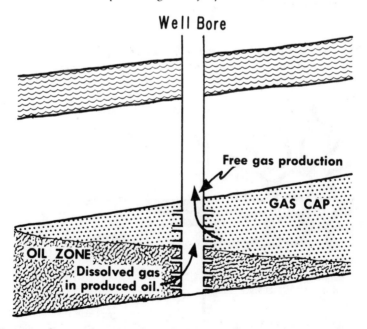

Fig. 84—*Gas produced with oil from associated gas cap and solution in the oil. (Courtesy* THE PETROLEUM ENGINEER—*Sept., 1956.)*

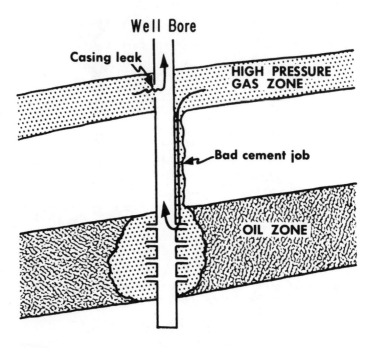

Fig. 85—*Free gas production from high pressure gas zone through casing leak and channel leak. (Courtesy* THE PETROLEUM ENGINEER—*Sept., 1956.)*

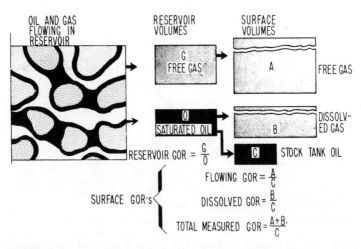

Fig. 86—*Gas-oil ratios under reservoir and surface measurements.*

certain point, relative permeability of the rock to oil diminishes rapidly and gas becomes the predominant fluid moving. Most of the original solution gas will be produced through this process as free gas flowing in the reservoir, although only a small portion of the oil originally in place is produced.

Produced gas is commonly thought of in terms of gas-oil ratio. To define various types of gas-oil ratios commonly considered, a schematic section of reservoir pore space is shown in Fig. 86. Both saturated oil and free gas are being produced from the sand so that total measured gas-oil ratio will be the sum in cubic feet of (a) free gas flowing in the reservoir and (b) dissolved gas in the oil flowing in the reservoir divided by (c) stock tank oil in barrels. If gas lift is being used as the artificial lift means in a field also experiencing free gas production, surface measurements of gas delivered from the wells will include spent gas-lift gas as well as produced gas. The gas-lift gas must be subtracted from the total to determine how much gas is actually produced along with the oil from the formation itself.

Another significant factor influencing amount of free gas production is the tendency of fluids to separate according to their

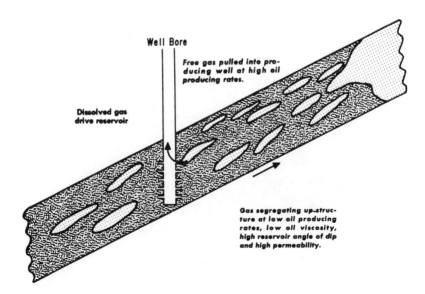

Fig. 87—*Effects of permeability, angle of dip, fluid viscosity and production rate on gravitational segregation of oil and gas in a reservoir.*

densities. Gravitational pull of the earth tends to cause liberated gas in the oil zone to flow upward and join the gas cap, or to form a gas cap if one is not already present. At the same time, the oil is pulled down from the gas-oil transition zone to the oil zone. As gas bubbles segregate upstructure, they may come within the pressure sinks surrounding wellbores. If pressure gradients into the well are great enough some of the gas will be pulled into the well and produced. Therefore, low producing rates for the wells with resulting low pressure drawdowns at wellbores and small diameter pressure sinks around the wells will help gravity move free gas to the high parts of the reservoir where energy in the compressed gas can be conserved (Fig. 87). On the other hand, gas will be drawn into the producing wells and less segregation will occur if the wells are being produced at high rates. This is caused by large pressure drawdowns and large pressure sinks around the wellbores, which hinder the gas from flowing on beyond the well to the gas cap. Other conditions which assist gravitational segregation are high permeability of

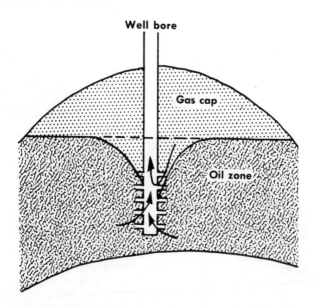

Fig. 88—*Coning of free gas into a well across bedding planes. (Courtesy* THE PETROLEUM ENGINEER—*Sept. 1956.)*

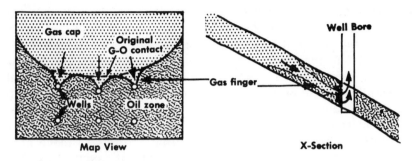

Fig. 89—*Fingering of free gas into well along bedding planes. (Courtesy* THE PETROLEUM ENGINEER—*Sept. 1956.)*

the sand, low viscosity of the oil and high angle of dip of the reservoir.

Gas-cap gas coning down across bedding planes (Fig. 88) and fingering down along bedding planes (Fig. 89) often occur in areas of excessive rates of oil withdrawals near the gas cap. What may be excessive oil production rates in one reservoir situation, however, may be entirely satisfactory in another; because the magnitude and variation of reservoir rock permeability,

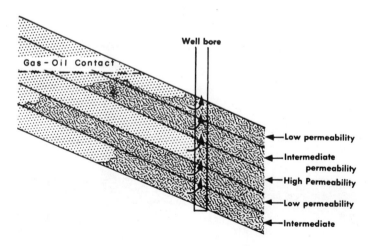

Fig. 90—*Irregular gas encroachment and early breakthrough of gas along high permeability layer of stratified reservoir. (Courtesy* THE PETROLEUM ENGINEER—*Sept., 1956.)*

oil viscosity and structural relief of the reservoir largely controls coning and fingering tendencies of gas from a gas cap.

The nature of the reservoir rock stratification is extremely important in maximum ultimate displacement of oil by the expanding drive of the gas cap. It is important to withdraw oil from all separate permeable layers of rock to permit the gas cap to expand through individual layers and displace the recoverable oil from each. Variation of permeability between layers of rock presents a problem, however, in getting the gas to move at a uniform rate of advance through the various layers. Gas that moves through high permeability strata and prematurely breaks through into producing wells will cause excessive gas-oil ratios before oil is recovered from the remainder of the strata. It is difficult to identify the source of such gas production for purposes of planning remedial work on the well (Fig. 90).

Length of the completion interval may influence the amount of gas coning into the wellbore. In some cases short completion intervals cause high pressure differentials between the wellbore and the source of free gas. In such cases cones and fingers of gas form easily (Fig. 91A). Longer completion intervals tend to reduce the pressure differential out into the oil reservoir, and

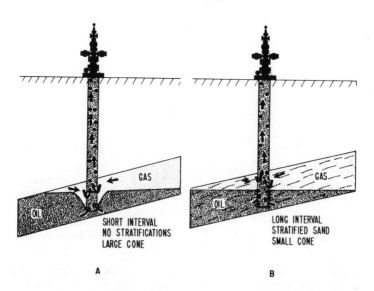

Fig. 91—*Effects of length of completion interval and stratification on coning.*

cones and fingers of gas caused by high pressure differentials may be reduced. Therefore, excess free gas production and its attendant loss in reservoir energy can be minimized at times through use of longer completion intervals.

Stratification materials in the reservoir tend to break vertical permeability abruptly and reduce coning of gas into the wellbore (Fig. 91B).

Water Production Trends

Water production is costly both from the standpoint of lifting produced water to the surface and then disposing of it. Maximum recovery from water drive reservoirs, however, requires that a large amount of water move through the sand; thus, large quantities of water production from the reservoir may be required eventually to assure maximum oil recoveries (Chapter 7). The operator, therefore, should not "run from water" or work wells over to exclude water unless reservoir study indicates that it is economically feasible.

Water disposal methods vary with volume of water produced and availability, cost and relative efficiency of the various

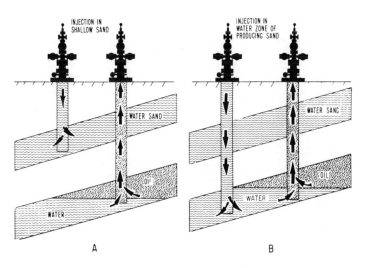

Fig. 92—*Disposal of produced water.*

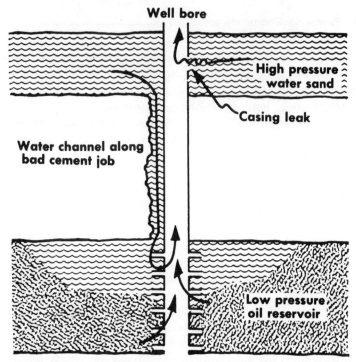

Fig. 93—*Water production from high pressure water zone through casing leak and channel leak. (Courtesy* THE PETROLEUM ENGINEER—*Sept., 1956.)*

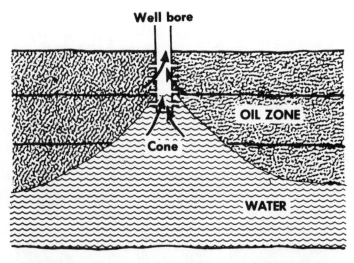

Fig. 94—*Coning of water into a well across bedding planes. (Courtesy* THE PETROLEUM ENGINEER—*Sept. 1956.)*

methods. In fields where produced volume of water is small such as from dissolved gas drive, gas cap drive, and combination drive reservoirs with limited water influx from the water basin, it may be possible to dispose of the water by evaporation from pits or disposal to tidewater. Drainage into streams is an excellent disposal means; however, the present-day pollution problem practically eliminates this as a satisfactory disposal method.

In fields producing from stronger water drive reservoirs where large volumes of water are produced, it is frequently necessary to use injection wells for disposal. Water can be injected into shallow low-pressure salt water sands or into the water basin below the producing reservoir as shown in Fig. 92. Injection of produced water into a shallow sand is usually economically accomplished with gravity injection or low-pressure injection wells. Injection into the water basin in strata from which oil is being produced frequently requires high injection pressures that utilize expensive disposal equipment. This type of injection, however, sometimes greatly enhances recovery efficiency of the reservoir and is usually employed when pressure maintenance provides economic benefits. An example of dual-purpose water return is the East Texas field project where such operations have maintained the Woodbine reservoir pressure above 1,000 psi for many years of continued production and have taken care of disposal of many millions of barrels of produced water.

There are sources of produced water other than the water drive of the reservoir itself. Examples are channeling of water along a poor primary cement job into the completion interval from an adjacent formation, either above or below the completion interval, and the leakage of water through casing failures if pressure in the formation opposite the leak is sufficient to cause water to flow from that formation into the wellbore (Fig. 93). In both of these examples, the produced water is contributing nothing toward flushing oil from the reservoir. Its production is totally undesirable; and, re-conditioning the well to reduce the increased operation expenses suffered through the handling of such water is usually justified.

Locating the source of produced water is facilitated in some fields by water analyses. It is good practice to take water samples from various formations penetrated during drilling operations to provide data for analysis. Where the difference in chemical composition of the various waters is sufficient, this is both a speedy and accurate method of determining whether produced water is coming from the oil producing formation. It is also a helpful indicator to guide the search for the channel or casing leak. In studying pressure and production trends of reservoirs and their relations to water production, it is important to know whether or not the water production is coming from the producing formation, since channeling or casing-leak water production could cause a completely erroneous interpretation of the reservoir drive mechanism.

The strength of a water drive, that is, the rate at which water flows into an oil reservoir operating under water drive, is governed by such things as difference in pressure between reservoir and aquifer, size of the aquifer, reservoir and aquifer permeability, amount of the reservoir adjacent and open to water entry, and whether the drive is by edge water or bottom water. If withdrawals from the reservoir are greater than the rate at which water can enter, reservoir pressure will decline. Likewise, excessive withdrawal rates from individual wells or low permeability areas will cause excessive pressure drawdowns between reservoir and wells, creating large pressure sinks around those wells. In a uniform sand, pressure sinks caused by high rates of fluid withdrawal can result in coning of water into the completion interval, as shown in Fig. 94. In a stratified sand, high rates of

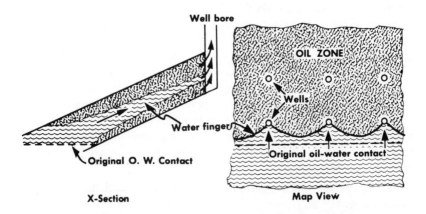

Fig. 95—*Fingering of water into well along bedding planes. (Courtesy* THE PETROLEUM ENGINEER—*Sept. 1956.)*

fluid withdrawal can result in water fingering along a high-permeability streak into the wells, as shown in Fig. 95, even though they are completed substantially above the water-oil contact. When a finger or a cone has reached a completion interval, it tends to become stable and to persist in continued water production because of reduced relative permeability to oil created by increased water saturation. In some wells, however, rock and fluid characteristics are such that the cone will subside if the producing rate is reduced. Development of fingers or cones of water on a widespread scale throughout the reservoir will usually reduce ultimate oil recovery because natural energy of the water drive is being used for production of water instead of forcing oil ahead of the water to the well. In addition, this premature water production will reduce profits by forcing earlier use

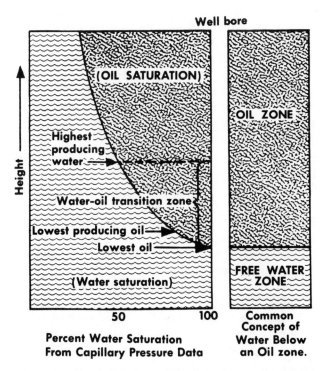

Fig. 96—*Water-oil transition zone defined as the zone between levels of lowest oil occurrence and highest water production. (Courtesy* THE PETROLEUM ENGINEER—*Sept., 1956.)*

of artificial lift equipment and requiring the handling of continually increasing volumes of salt water to obtain the same amount of oil production.

An oil-water contact does not occur as a horizonal plane at a specific depth; instead, there is a zone of transition from the level of 100-per cent water saturation upward to some minimum water saturation above the 100-per cent level. Fig. 96 shows schematically the distribution of water and oil saturations as they occur in the reservoir rock. Although there is some oil saturation all the way down as indicated by the lowest arrow, a well completed between the middle and lower arrow would produce 100 per cent water. This will occur because the rock has no permeability to oil at the low oil saturations that exist in this zone. The lack of permeability results from the fact that oil exists as separate droplets trapped by interfacial forces (Chapter 7). A well completed above the top arrow will produce pipe line oil because water saturation above this point is less than that necessary to permit water flow. A well completed between the top and center arrows will produce both water and oil because of intermediate saturation conditions and relative permeabilities resulting from those saturations. The transition zone then will be defined as the zone between the levels of lowest oil occurrence and highest water production.

From physical occurence of the transition zone and the manner in which production is influenced by the transitional nature of the fluid saturations, the expressions "oil-water" or "gas-oil contacts" are therefore quite arbitrary in meaning. General practice in the past has been to consider the transition zone as a plane of contact below which one fluid and above which another will be produced. This practice, however, is not always adequate in solving reservoir problems, for here the true physical factors must be recognized and utilized. An understanding of transition zones will be helpful in solving water production problems for some individual wells. If the completion interval selected lies in a transition zone, it would obviously be of no benefit to squeeze-cement and reperforate a well in the transition zone, for the well will continue to produce some water. It may, however, be proper to squeeze-cement and recomplete the well above the transition zone for water-free oil production, but as in most well remedial work the economics of such work will dictate its feasibility.

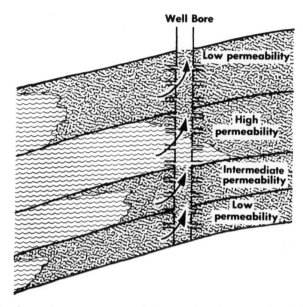

Fig. 97—*Irregular water encroachment and early water breakthrough in high permeability layers of reservoir rock. (Courtesy* THE PETROLEUM ENGINEER—*Sept., 1956.)*

Frequently the reservoir is composed of overlying beds of different permeabilities separated by impermeable layers such that water advances at different rates through the different beds (Fig. 97). It is important to withdraw oil from all separate permeable layers of rock to permit the water to move through individual layers and displace oil from each. Even though early breakthrough of water in the high permeability beds may not cause premature abandonment, a large volume of water must be produced before the oil is depleted from the other beds. Water which moves through only part of the strata and breaks through prematurely into producing wells may contact the other producing layers of rock at the wellbore and tend to reduce oil production by water blocking those layers. The economic length of completion intervals is determined by comparing the cost of lifting large quantities of water produced through long completion intervals with the cost of several extra well workover jobs utilizing shorter completion intervals.

♦

♦

♦

How Oil Is Displaced
Naturally from Reservoirs

The drainage of oil from the porous rock to producing wells occurs to a small extent because compressed rock, water and oil relax and expand when the high subsurface pressure is reduced through oil production. (See Chapter 5.) A large portion of the reservoir oil, however, must be replaced by some fluid; oil cannot be removed from its initial location in the rock pore space unless something takes its place. Therefore, the drainage of oil occurs naturally to a major degree because water or gas moves through the pore spaces in which the oil occurs and displaces a portion of that oil ahead of the displacing fluid to the wellbore. For maximum effect it is important that the displacing fluids move through the greatest number of oil-filled pore spaces. In this way, the greatest number of pore spaces will contribute oil, and maximum oil recovery from the reservoir thereby can be attained.

Oil recovery by gas and water displacement can best be illustrated by observing what happens inside an individual pore channel during displacement. Fig. 98 illustrates two separate pore channels of different size, occuring in the oil reservoir when discovered. The large channel represents higher, and the small, lower permeability. Connate water is located adjacent to the sand grains, while oil occupies the middle of the pore channel. Reservoirs with fluids distributed in this manner are termed water-

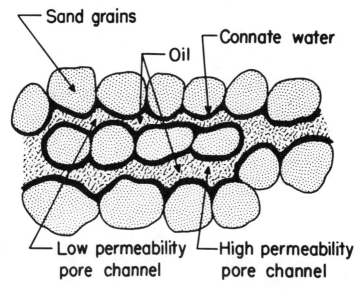

Fig. 98—*Original oil and water saturations in pore space at equilibrium. (Courtesy* JOURNAL OF PETROLEUM TECHNOLOGY—*June, 1958.)*

wet, a classification to which a large majority belong. A minority of reservoir rocks are considered by some to be oil-wet. Although little definitely is known about the distribution of fluids in oil-wet rocks, it generally is believed that connate water is present in much smaller quantities in oil-wet rock than in water-wet rock. The water-wet rock system will be discussed in this chapter because of its more general application.

In the gas displacement process, gas tends to move through the middle of the pore channels because gas does not wet the sand. An inefficient displacement and relatively low recovery of oil results (Fig. 99). In a water-wet system, on the other hand, water forms a cup-like oil-water interface which tends to displace all the oil from a given point in the pore channel (Fig. 100). Although a number of factors are involved, rock wettability is thus shown to reflect considerable influence on the manner in which oil is displaced; if the rock is preferentially water-wet, water displacement will be much more efficient than gas displacement.

All oil-bearing porous rocks exhibit variations in size and shape of the pore spaces. These variations further control the degree of oil recovery from the rocks. Under the gas displacement process, gas tends to move easily through large pore channels because of its low viscosity and great mobility. As the gas moves through the sand, much of the residual oil tends to remain in the low permeability pore channels (Fig. 101). Because great quantities of mobile, low viscosity gas can move easily through only a few pore channels, gas drive alone usually results in a low percentage of oil recovered. Where the volume of gas present is

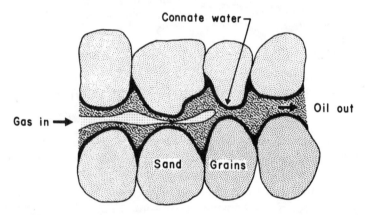

Fig. 99—*Natural displacement of oil by gas in a single pore channel. (Courtesy* JOURNAL OF PETROLEUM TECHNOLOGY—*June, 1958.)*

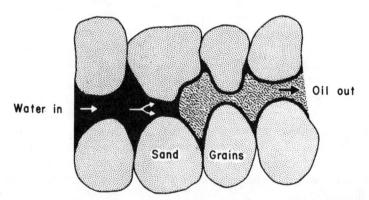

Fig. 100—*Natural displacement of oil by water in a single pore channel. (Courtesy* JOURNAL OF PETROLEUM TECHNOLOGY—*June, 1958.)*

quite low, as in the case of dissolved gas drive reservoirs, oil recovery is quite low.

A different kind of recovery mechanism is present under water drive. The capillary forces cause water to move faster into

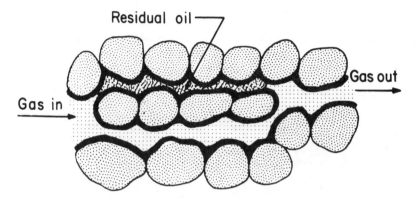

Fig. 101—*Gas displaces oil first from high permeability pore channels. Residual oil occurs in lower permeability pore channels. (Courtesy* Journal of Petroleum Technology—*June, 1958.)*

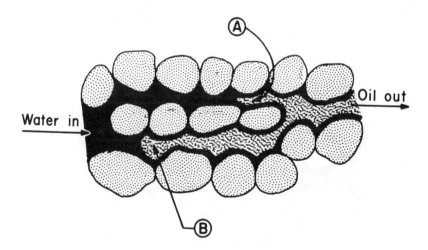

Fig. 102—*Capillary forces cause water to move ahead faster in low permeability pore channel (A) when water is moving slow through high permeability pore channel (B). (Courtesy* Journal of Petroleum Technology—*June, 1958.)*

the smaller, low permeability channels (Fig. 102). As water saturation builds up in the large pore channel and oil saturation is reduced, the oil present tends to take the shape of a smaller thread of oil (Fig. 103). As this thread gets smaller, the interfacial tension increases until the surface snaps at Points A and B along the pore channel, thus forming small droplets of oil behind the point where the film breaks. Their diameters are greater than the diameter of the oil thread before it broke be-

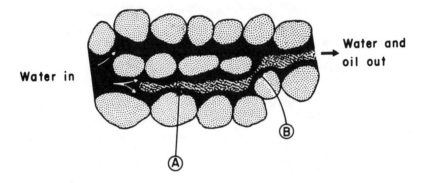

Fig. 103—*As thread of oil gets smaller, interfacial tension increases in the film at restricted Points A and B, where film subsequently breaks. (Courtesy* JOURNAL OF PETROLEUM TECHNOLOGY—*June, 1958.)*

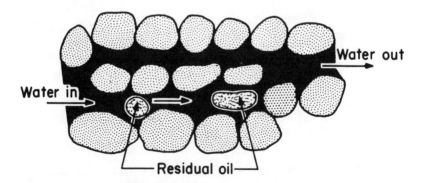

Fig. 104—*Water drive leaves residual oil in sand because surface films break at restrictions in sand pore channels. (Courtesy* JOURNAL OF PETROLEUM TECHNOLOGY—*June, 1958.)*

cause the tension in the oil-water surface causes the droplets to be spherical instead of thread-like. The spherical droplets then remain trapped within the pore spaces because their surface tension is greater than the forces acting to push them through the smaller pore channels (Fig. 104). A large part of the residual oil in the reservoir will be trapped in the pore channels by the interfacial forces inherent between water and oil.

Another important feature of water displacement of oil occurs in the case of oil-filled dead-end pore channels (Fig. 105). High capillary pressure gradients occur from inside these pore channels, causing the oil to be ejected through the center of the pore channel and water to be imbibed along the surface of the sand grains. This process of water imbibition causes oil to move into high permeability portions of the rock where it can be displaced with frontal water drive to the wellbore.

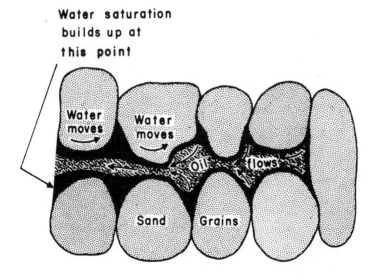

Fig. 105—*Capillary pressure gradient causes oil to move out and water to move into a dead-end pore channel when sand is water-wet. (Courtesy* JOURNAL OF PETROLEUM TECHNOLOGY—*June, 1958.)*

Oil Displacement from Reservoir Rock

Technically, no rocks should be termed "uniform" rocks. In practice, however, uniform reservoir rocks have come to be known as such in a relative way because their pore spaces vary little in size and generally are interconnected. Permeability of these uniform rocks does not vary greatly over distances of a few inches or many feet. More important still is the fact that uniform rocks react fairly uniformly to either water or gas as a displacing fluid so that these fluids can move consistently through the rock.

The history of displacement of oil from a block of uniform sand by water is illustrated diagrammatically in Fig. 106. Water and oil saturations occurring at original conditions in a reservoir are illustrated in Fig. 106A. The bottom of the block of sand

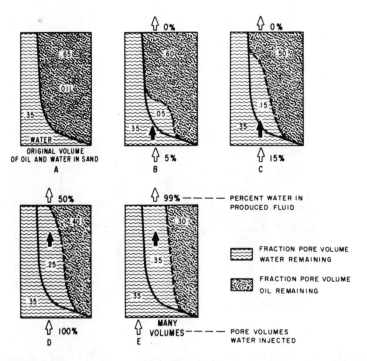

Fig. 106—*Steps showing changes in oil and water saturations in a clean uniform sand during oil displacement by water drive.*

represents the free water level in the reservoir where water completely fills the pore spaces. Oil saturation increases with height above that level (water saturation decreases) until uniformly low water saturation or "connate-water saturation" occurs over a given interval of height. This is represented along the upper part of the block of sand in Fig. 106A.

The displacement of oil from the sand by water does not occur strictly in a piston fashion, as is often thought. As water is injected at the bottom of the sand (Fig. 106B) and moves through the sand, it appears as a bank with saturations increasing rapidly from the front of the bank, where the connate-water saturation occurs, down to a point where about 60 to 65 per cent water saturation occurs. The water saturation increases only slightly thereafter down to the injection face of the sand block, where 100 per cent water saturation occurred originally. Water-free oil continues to be produced (Fig. 106C) until the water bank reaches the top or out-flow face of the sand. Thereafter, water commences to be produced, increasing rapidly at first until it reaches 50 to 70 per cent in the produced fluid (Fig. 106D). As more and more water is injected, the water percentage in the produced fluid continues to increase; correspondingly, a gradual decrease in oil saturation in the sand takes place (Fig. 106E). This continues until finally no more oil is produced with the water. At this point, however, considerable oil is left distributed as a residual saturation throughout the sand.

There are several important features of this displacement action. Considerable amounts of water must be flowed through the oil-bearing rock to obtain maximum oil. Practical depletion of oil from reservoir rock is determined on the basis of economics and occurs at the time when the amount of water in the production gets so high as to be uneconomical to lift, produce and dispose of. The presence of 100 per cent water production does not mean that only water remains in the rock. Under natural displacement methods, a considerable amount of oil is left in the rock. The appearance of water in a producing well, although bad from the standpoint of the problems of water production, does not mean that the production of oil is over. To obtain all the producible oil, it is necessary to continue to produce large quantities of water from a well unless other wells are completed so that the oil can be produced farther upstructure. In any event, the highest producing wells eventually will require large amounts of water production before the reservoir is depleted of its producible oil. Therefore, the cost involved in lifting large quantities of water provides the limiting factor in determining how much oil can be recovered from the reservoir.

Displacement of Oil from Non-uniform Sand

In the displacement of oil from reservoir rock, the displacing action should take place in the greatest number of pore spaces possible and should utilize the most efficient displacing fluid. Under most conditions, especially in water-wet rocks, water usually will be the most efficient natural displacing fluid; therefore, natural water drive is usually utilized if practical. The following discussion, therefore, will center on water displacement, although gas displacement is similar in many respects.

Natural reservoirs are never completely uniform. The reservoir rock may exist as successive layers, each of which may be relatively uniform but may vary between layers in permeability and other characteristics. The non-uniformity may be a lateral variation (that is, not continuous) because rock in one area has different properties from rock in other areas of the same layer. These lateral variations may exist within a single large area comprising an entire reservoir or as numerous small lenses completely enclosed by rock of different permeability or by shales with no permeability at all. The non-uniformity results from the manner in which the sediments were deposited and their environment during geologic history.

Area Swept — Pattern

As water advances into the oil-bearing rock, it tends to advance more rapidly through the more permeable rock, regardless of rock configuration. In moving across a reservoir, therefore, the water or gas fronts may tend to by-pass entire areas because of the pressure differentials from well to well and the shape of the reservoir as defined by shale barriers or rock with low permeabilities. After the displacing material has moved across the reservoir and all the wells have been abandoned, there still may be isolated areas in the reservoir through which the displacing fluid did not move and displace oil (Fig. 107). If 70 per cent of the total original reservoir volume has been included in the area of the drive's influence, pattern efficiency is conisdered to be 70 per cent. To obtain the highest oil recovery from reservoirs, therefore, requires development and operation so that water or gas as displacing material will actually move across the greatest area of the oil zone. Many factors control pattern efficiency. The more significant ones include well location with respect to the reservoir limits, structural dip, production rates, mobility of water compared to reservoir oil, and rock uniformity.

Section Swept — Conformance

It is necessary to flow water through all tight sections, lenses, layers or spots within the reservoir to achieve displacement of oil from the maximum number of pore spaces. The degree to which a reservoir is flooded within the pattern area is considered its conformance. All reservoir volume within the pattern area,

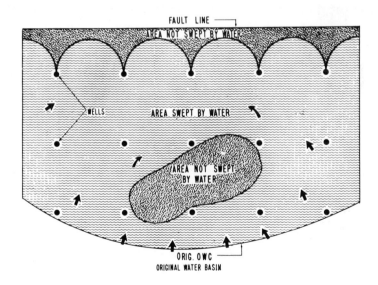

Fig. 107—*Pattern efficiency of displacement by water drive.*

whether tight or highly permeable, is included in the determination of this factor. Conformance will be 100 per cent if water moves through all the pore spaces in the pattern area of rock. Conformance will be 70 per cent if water by-passes 30 per cent of the total rock volume within the pattern area (Fig. 108).

The conformance efficiency, or factor, will not be the same for water displacement as for gas displacement in a given reservoir because many factors are different in the two cases. Among the factors that influence conformance efficiency by a given drive and also the difference in conformance efficiency between drives for a given reservoir rock are location of producing wells, wettability of the rock, angle of dip of the reservoir, rate of production, mobility of the displacing fluid compared to that of reservoir oil, degree of reservoir rock uniformity,and capillary imbibition factors which affect entry of displacing fluid into tight lenses.

Effects of Rate on Capillary Displacement

Rate of oil displacement is defined as the rate of movement of the interface between the displacing fluid and oil, or the rate of movement of the displacing front. This is related to well producing rates in a general way—and then only by a combination

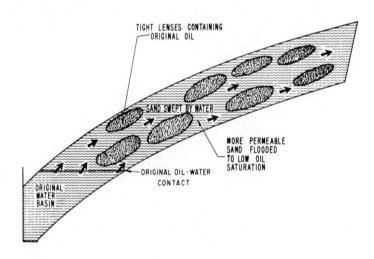

Fig. 108—*Conformance efficiency of displacement by water drive.*

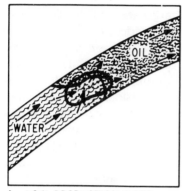 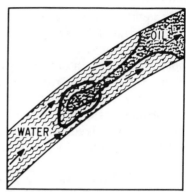

A - LOW PRODUCTION RATE
HIGH RECOVERY

B - HIGH PRODUCTION RATE
LOW RECOVERY

Fig. 109—*Effect of rate on capillary displacement of oil from tight sand lenses.*

of factors such as well spacing, reservoir thickness, porosity, water saturation, geometry of the reservoir, area of contact between the displacing fluid and oil, etc.

Capillary forces tend to cause water to distribute throughout all of the rock and even to enter the tight segments of the rock. This tendency may be slow acting, however, so that at lower rates of movement water is imbibed by these capillary forces into the tighter pore spaces; thus, oil is forced into larger pore channels where it is carried to the well and produced (Fig. 109A). If the rate of displacement is too fast, imbibition of water into the tight lenses may be overshadowed by the fast rate of displacement in the permeable sections. Although the water front has moved on past the tight lenses (Fig. 109B), oil is continuously ejected from the tight sections by the capillary forces. The continuous ejection of oil from the tight pores to flowing channels necessarily scatters small individual droplets throughout the water behind the flood front. Unless it arrives at the producing well before high water cuts force abandonment, however, this oil will be lost. It is necessary, therefore, to produce water drive reservoirs at such a rate that water will have time to be absorbed into the tighter lenses by capillary forces, thus displacing oil to the flowing streams where it can be produced before water production causes abandonment of producing wells.

In general, the slower the rate, the greater will be the recovery from the tight sections of sand (provided, of course, other factors are not detrimental to recovery at slower rates). After displacement rate has been lowered to a certain point, however, further reductions in rate will result in only negligible increases in recovery. Displacement rate can be considered relative, and the optimum rate is dictated by the reservoir itself. Since many factors are involved in the displacement efficiency, considerable variation may exist in the optimum rates of different reservoirs.

How Capillary Forces Act to Displace
Oil from Low Permeability Lenses

The reason capillary forces cause water to be absorbed in tight or low permeability lenses of reservoir rock is illustrated in Fig. 102. It is shown that the radius of curvature of the interfacial film between water and oil at Point A is much smaller than at Point B. With greater curvature at Point A, a higher pressure is built up across the interfacial film at Point A than across the interfacial film at Point B. The oil tends to be driven out of the low permeability portion of the rock by the higher pressure existing in the water-oil interface, while the high permeability portion of the rock does not have as great a driving force operating to expel oil from its pores. If low permeability pore channels are scattered among high permeability channels, capillary forces tend to cause water to rapidly enter them first. On the other hand, if the low permeability channels are segregated as large volumes of rock or tight lenses, water flow into and oil flow out of the lenses will be delayed by the permeability difference and the distance through which the displacing water must move. To obtain maximum oil from the low permeability lenses, some time delay in production must be made so that the capillary forces can act to denude the tighter lenses of their oil before the displacing water front moves past the lenses (Fig. 109).

Effects of Bed Thickness and Permeability
on Capillary Displacement

Frequently the reservoir is composed of overlying layers of

rock in capillary contact or equilibrium, but having different permeabilities. Fig. 110 shows the effects of bed thickness and permeability on displacement of oil by water drive. The thin, low permeability bed shown in Fig. 110A can be easily displaced of its oil by the lateral effects of capillary forces because these forces have only a short distance to move oil into the flowing streams of the high permeability rock. The thick, low permeability layer shown in Fig. 110B presents more of a problem because capillary forces must move the oil further to flowing streams in the high permeability rock layers. Even though capillary forces may permit high displacement efficiency in the thick, low permeability bed, lower displacement rates and thus longer time periods are

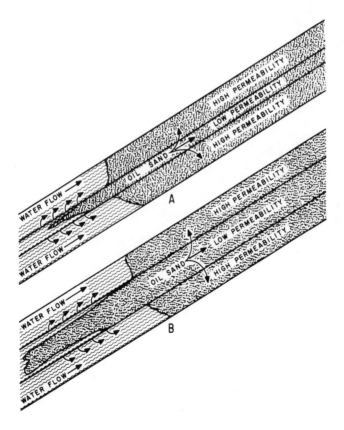

Fig. 110—*Effects of permeability and bed thickness on oil displacement by water*

usually required. If the bed is sufficiently thick, it may require closer spacing of wells and completion within the tight bed only.

Fig. 111 shows the case of gas cap drive. Oil viscosity, the purging action of gas and gravity drainage (rather than capillary effects) are the important factors which tend to control the oil-displacing action of gas.

Multiple Reservoirs

Frequently the reservoir is composed of overlying beds of different properties that are separated by layers of shale (Figs. 90

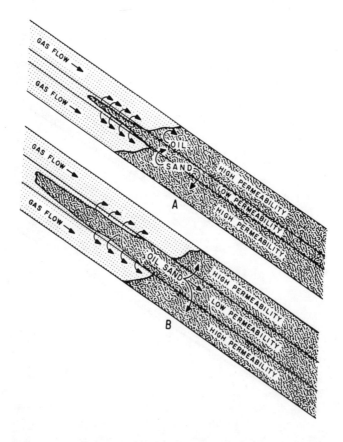

Fig. 111—*Effects of permeability and bed thickness on oil displacement by gas.*

and 97). Because shale usually has little or no permeability, capillary forces cannot cause fluids to move from bed to bed across the shale layers; the two permeable beds may be separate reservoirs. Water can advance more rapidly in the more permeable bed. If variation in permeability between beds is high, water may approach a well completion through the high permeability bed long before water approaches the well in the other beds (Fig. 97). This stratification problem presents great difficulties in oil production by both water and gas drives. The sand, originally water-wet, tends to absorb water back into the low permeability layers at the wellbore. In this manner, some of these strata may be shut off as oil producers before their oil is recovered from the well, thus trapping large quantities of oil out in the reservoir. In the case of gas drive, once free gas has broken through high-permeability strata, it may be virtually impossible to produce any further oil from the remaining, lower permeability strata because of the ease with which gas moves through the gassed-out section and is produced.

Proper completion in stratified sands is an economic problem, and the operator must compare the expense of (1) several workovers and recompletions in individual zones with (2) the lower workover expense but higher lifting costs incurred in production of several zones simultaneously through a single completion (which, by inefficient use of reservoir energy, may reduce ultimate recovery).

Over-all Reservoir Oil Recovery

High reservoir oil recoveries occur as a result of a combination of high pattern, high conformance and high displacement efficiencies; therefore, to produce a reservoir in the best manner, such reservoir must have had its oil displaced by a closely controlled drive so that maximum efficiency of these three factors can be effected. The locations of wells producing from the rock, together with the non-uniformity of the reservoir and operating practices, combine to determine not only the amount of reservoir rock through which water advances but, also, the efficiency of displacement occurring in that portion of the rock through which water moves. Obtaining maximum recovery efficiencies by natural drives, therefore, requires that the operator completely understand the reservoir and its drive mechanism to properly plan and control reservoir production operations.

Influence of Oil Shrinkage on Recovery

Final shrinkage conditions of residual oil left in a reservoir rock following depletion influences, within limits, the amount of oil recovered. A barrel of oil under pressure conditions near original reservoir pressure will represent something less than 1 stock tank barrel at the surface. On the other hand, if reservoir oil pressure at depletion conditions is quite low (or near atmospheric pressure), each barrel of residual oil in the reservoir represents nearly 1 barrel of stock tank oil. This is true because at low pressure the solution gas has been liberated and a given volume of original oil has shrunk. A given residual oil saturation or a given volume of oil in the reservoir rock will represent dif-

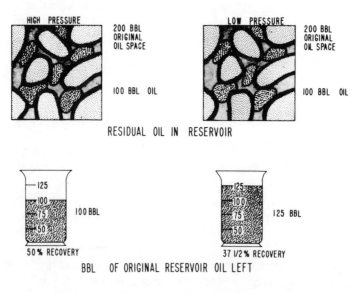

Fig. 112—*Loss in oil recovery through shrinkage.*

ferent stock tank volumes under different conditions of shrinkage as determined by differing abandonment pressures. Therefore, shrinkage affects recovery by giving higher recoveries at
higher abandonment saturation pressures for a given saturation
of oil left in the reservoir. Fig. 112 shows that, for the condition
chosen, a residual oil saturation of 50 per cent of original oil-
filled pore space means that 50 per cent of original oil is left in
the rock if pressure is maintained at original conditions and that
$62\frac{1}{2}$ per cent of original oil is left in the rock if the pressure
drops to a low value. Thus, 50 per cent recovery is obtained if
pressure is maintained at initial reservoir pressure conditions,
and $37\frac{1}{2}$ per cent recovery is obtained if pressure is allowed to
drop—yet in both cases, the same displacement efficiency by the
reservoir drive is obtained.

Influence of Oil Viscosity on Recovery

The viscosities of oil and its displacing fluids play important roles in determining the ease with which oil is pushed
through the pore space of reservoir sands and the degree to
which oil is permitted to stick to the reservoir sand grains to
remain as residual oil. Just as in pipe lines, highly viscous oils
do not move easily. When pushed by a fluid of lower viscosity,
the high viscosity oil preferentially sticks to the walls of pore
channels and permits the low viscosity displacing fluid to move
ahead. Low oil recoveries generally are obtained, therefore, from
reservoirs where oil viscosity is high. The viscosity of oil changes
with a drop in pressure and depends to a large degree on the
change in density as pressure drops and gas is liberated. When
pressure drops, light components leave the mixture to form the
gas phase, and the remaining oil is heavier. As a consequence of
this change, oil viscosity increases (Fig. 113). The increase in its
viscosity causes oil to become less mobile, or to move with greater
difficulty in the reservoir. It is desirable, therefore, to prevent the
gas from coming out of solution in the reservoir; this can be
accomplished by preventing a drop in reservoir pressure.

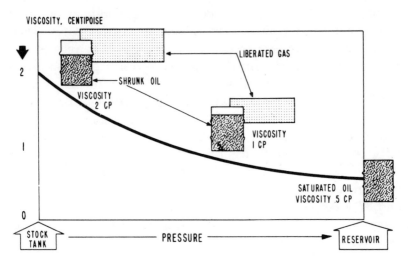

Fig. 113—*Effects of solution gas on viscosity.*

Influence of Dissolved Gas on Recovery

The gas in solution in dissolved gas drive reservoirs, when liberated as pressure drops, provides the displacing action which permits oil recovery. Considering this factor alone—the more gas in solution, the greater should be the energy to displace oil. However, the degree of oil shrinkage also is dependent upon the quantity of gas in solution; the greater the amount of gas in solution, the greater will be the degree of oil shrinkage as that gas is liberated. The quantity of dissolved gas in the oil also influences oil viscosity because, as gas is removed from the oil, viscosity of oil will increase. Increase in shrinkage and viscosity characteristics of oil will tend to reduce oil recovery, thereby offsetting the tendency toward increased recovery afforded by the presence of large amounts of dissolved gas. Usually, sufficient gas is dissolved in oils saturated at comparatively low pressures for a rather normal dissolved gas drive to be present; however by comparison to the other drive mechanisms, its recovery efficiency is quite low.

◆

◆

◆

Developing and Operating Oil Reservoirs for Maximum Recovery

The fundamental objective in the production and operation of petroleum reservoirs is to produce the maximum percentage of the deposit while at the same time attempting to keep initial investment and operating expenses at the lowest level possible to obtain this recovery. The variations in development programs and operating practices which may be proposed for a reservoir are many and may be widely divergent in cost, so that an optimum point lies within the range of recoveries which may be obtained under the several programs. The physical characteristics of the reservoir and its fluids determine the maximum economic recovery; however, consideration also must be given the laws, rules and regulations under which the producer must operate.

Within this complex set of conditions, the petroleum engineer must investigate and answer many vital questions so that sound decisions, based upon economics, may be made. Fortunately, many of the reservoir factors influencing final decisions are determinate and with the governing rules and regulations defined, investment and operating costs may be projected within reasonable limits. The main factors, however, deal with the reservoir itself and the development program and operating procedures to be used in its exploitation.

Previous discussions have dealt with some of the fundamental reservoir characteristics and operating problems directly related to the development and operation of oil reservoirs for maximum economic recovery. Chapter 5 pointed out that the three basic types of recovery mechanisms provide widely varying efficiency—not only between the mechanisms but within a single drive category. Individual well performance may be a function of drive mechanism or natural reservoir rock and fluid characteristics (Chapter 6). Proper utilization of well spacing, structural position, reservoir characteristics, drive mechanism, conservation of reservoir energy and secondary operations all influence recovery efficiency and well performance.

The potential effect of each of these factors on the ultimate oil recovery, field life expectancy and costs must be considered. Variations in spacing, optimum well location and energy conservation should therefore be investigated for their effects in increasing recovery and lowering costs. Finally an optimum program can be designed that will recover the greatest amount of oil at the least cost.

Development of Reservoirs

It is frequently possible to have some idea of the type of drive to be expected, even before a new field is discovered, if the wildcat is located in an area where other fields are producing. A knowledge of the geology of the area and the producing horizon will permit some immediate conclusions to be drawn. For example, continuity of the producing formation or existence of major faults will determine the extent of the water basin which is available to provide water drive. Geophysical data on the structure may indicate the type of trap. Drill-stem tests, logs, and cores on wildcat wells may indicate whether or not a gas cap or a water table is penetrated. These data together with the behavior characteristics of older fields producing from the same sand should permit some interpretation of the drive to be expected.

Location of well completions will definitely affect the degree of control over the recovery mechanism; therefore, it is economically advantageous to develop a field in a manner that will not only take advantage of the most efficient drive available, but also afford the fullest possible degree of control over the drive. Rock characteristics such as permeability, storage capacity or porosity and formation thickness should provide guides to optimum well spacing, whether or not flowing wells may be expected.

Basis of Development Programs

Money, time, labor and materials consumed in drilling wells are largely non-recoverable; therefore, if development drilling proceeds on close spacing before the drive is correctly identified, the investment will already be made when the recovery mechanism is finally determined. This does not present an impossible problem, even when the predominant drive cannot be determined early in

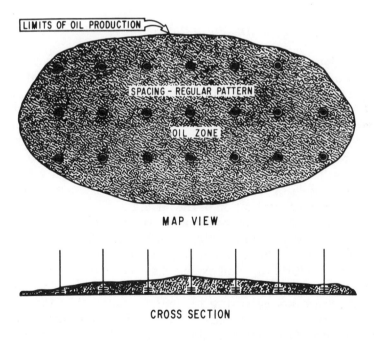

MAP VIEW

CROSS SECTION

Fig. 114—*Dissolved gas drive reservoir—low angle of dip.*

development. A certain number of wells must be drilled in any event if the field is of appreciable size. Enough wells are needed to define the reservoir—that is, to locate the periphery and established oil-water and gas-oil contacts. Additional wells will usually be required by lease and offset obligations. Beyond this minimum, the number of infill wells and the well spacing can be varied in many instances. When possible, the development program should be based on reservoir considerations and conditions, rather than on surface conditions or on some arbitrary grid pattern. The development program can be outlined schematically with subsurface stratigraphic cross-sections and a surface plan for well locations on the structure map.

Small fields, or small leases, and competitive conditions, however, often prevent such an ideal plan of development. Under competitive conditions, it is highly desirable that all operators cooperate early in formulating prudent and intelligent development plans. Figs. 114 through 120 illustrate some factors of a reservoir nature that influence well spacing and location of completion intervals.

Dissolved Gas Drive

Well spacing may be on a regular pattern throughout the oil zone in a dissolved gas drive reservoir with low structural relief (Fig. 114). Such reservoirs are formed by permeability pinching out or faulting around the periphery of the reservoir. Provided the reservoir rock is not stratified, the completion intervals should be located in the lower part of the oil column. Low completions would tend to help gravity segregation, permit a gas cap to form from gas liberated from the oil and thereby augment recovery. Very low angle of dip would, however, minimize assistance derived by gravity segregation of the oil and gas.

A regular spacing pattern could also be used for a dissolved gas drive reservoir with a high angle of dip (Fig. 115). Again the completion intervals would be structurally low because of the angle of structural dip, and exact subsurface location would vary with well location on the structure. Here it is expected that the oil will drain downstructure in time so that higher than usual oil recovery may be realized with minimum investment in wells. The operator must recognize the reservoir situation soon enough, however, to eliminate drilling the structurally high wells.

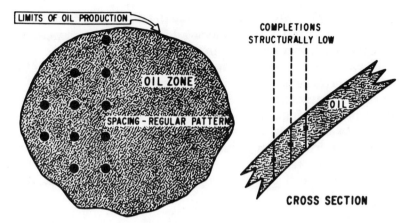

Fig. 115—*Dissolved gas drive reservoir—high angle of dip.*

Gas Cap Drive Reservoirs

Wells may be spaced on a regular pattern in a gas cap drive reservoir where sand is thick, dip angle is low and the gas cap is completely underlain by oil (Fig. 116). Again completions should be made low in the section to permit the gas cap to expand and drive oil down to the completion intervals for maximum recovery with minimum gas production. This type of pure gas cap drive might be found where the limits of the field are defined by faulting or pinchouts of the permeable reservoir rock adjacent to impermeable shale and limestone formations.

A gas cap drive reservoir in a thin sand with a high angle of dip is likely to be more efficiently controlled by having completions spaced irregularly but low on the structure to conform to the shape of the reservoir (Fig. 117). Because of the high angle of dip, a regular spacing pattern may cause many completions to be located too near the gas-oil contact. Such an oil reservoir is common where multiple thin sands are found on a single structure and the oil column is only a fraction of the total productive reservoir relief.

Water Drive Reservoirs

Wells may be spaced on a regular pattern in a water drive reservoir having a thick sand and low angle of dip (Fig. 118).

Completion intervals, however, should be selected high on the structure to permit long producing life while oil is displaced up to completion intervals by the invading water.

A water drive reservoir in a thin sand with high angle of dip may best be developed with irregular well spacing because of the structural characteristics (Fig. 119). The completions, however, should be made high on the structure to delay encroachment of water into the producing wells. Spotting the wells on a regular spacing pattern not only may cause a number of the wells to produce water early in the life of the reservoir and result in their early abandonment but also may reduce the effectiveness of the

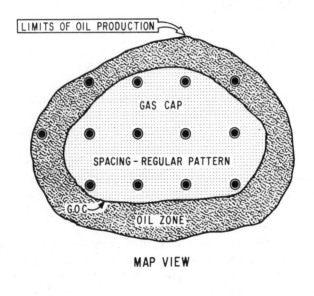

MAP VIEW

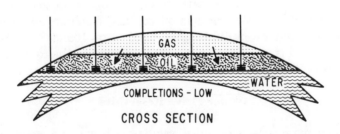

CROSS SECTION

Fig. 116—*Gas cap drive reservoir—low angle of dip.*

water drive through excessive early water production. Fewer wells would then remain to produce the remainder of the oil, thus lengthening unnecessarily the time required to deplete the reservoir.

Combination Drive

A combination drive reservoir in a thin sand, as shown in Fig. 120, illustrates several important points. View A shows the reservoir divided into two parts. If it is known that water drive will be predominant in a rim-type reservoir of this nature, completion should be made high on the structure. On the other hand, if the supporting water basin is known to be small and a weak water drive is indicated, gas cap drive would control reser-

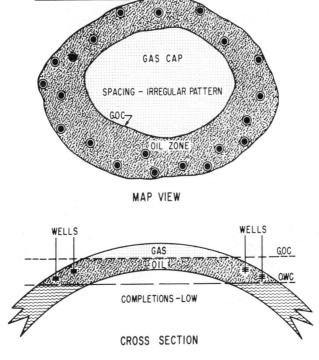

Fig. 117—*Gas cap drive reservoir—high angle of dip.*

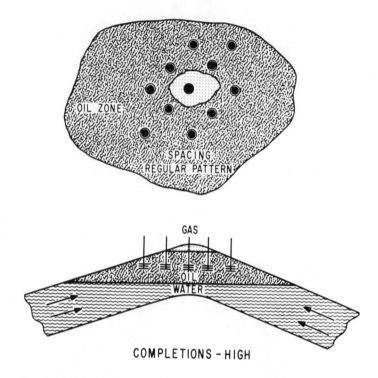

Fig. 118—*Water drive reservoir—low angle of dip, thick sand.*

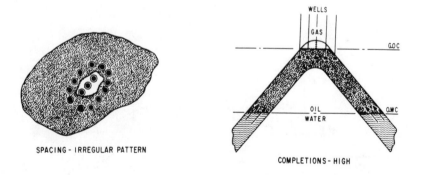

Fig. 119—*Water drive reservoir—high angle of dip, thin sand.*

voir behavior. Under these conditions, it would be desirable to make the completions low on the structure.

An alternative development program would employ a surface grid pattern, as shown in View B, if it is impossible at first to decide whether the gas cap or the water drive would predominate. The major disadvantage of the grid pattern is that all high wells would be invaded by the expanding gas early in their producing lives if the gas cap drive is later found to predominate. They would produce at high gas-oil ratios with low recovery efficiency or with penalized allowable, thus limiting recovery obtained for investment made in each well. On the other hand, if the water drive predominated, edge wells would suffer earlier water invasion and lower recovery than they might have achieved had they been completed structurally higher.

The best general approach is first to drill suitable wells, regardless of the operating drive, and infill or expand the drilling program when the drive has been identified. No rule-of-thumb can be used because the physical and producing characteristics of the reservoir dictate proper well locations. The first and most important problem to answer is the nature of the complex reser-

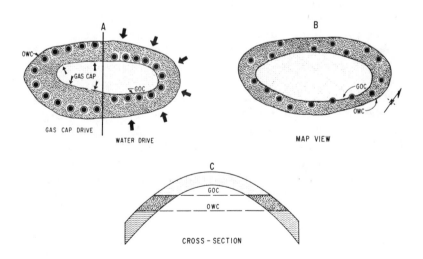

Fig. 120—*Rim-type reservoir—various drives, thin sand.*

voir producing characteristics on which development of the reservoir can be based.

Sand Uniformity

The general procedure, as shown by the illustrations, is to complete high for water drive and low for gas cap and dissolved gas drives—to have an adequate number but not too many wells. It would be practical, however, to make such completions only if the sand were quite uniform. If the sand is stratified either by shale breaks or by variation in permeability, it probably will be necessary to stagger the completion intervals in various members of the reservoir to be sure that each member is drained. Some vertical staggering of completion intervals can be effected during development to secure proportionate withdrawals from the various strata. Additional distribution of completions between the various members of the pay may then be made during later workover programs on the basis of experience and competitive operational conditions.

For maximum recovery from reservoir completions, intervals should be limited to one identifiable zone wherever practical. Length of the interval should be held to that required for anticipated producing rate without causing excessive pressure drawdown, which might lead to premature coning or fingering of gas or water into the wellbore. Single-zone completions are preferred to facilitate thorough flushing for higher recoveries and obtain flexibility in recompletion work for control of reservoir performance.

Completions comprising more than one of a group of reservoir members are generally termed multizone completions. Such completions may be needed for very low permeability sands which require long completion intervals for obtaining economic quantities of production. Multizone completions may also be economically desirable in latter stages of depletion of a complex reservoir where pressures are low in all zones.

Migration

The best producing drive will be of little help to an operator in obtaining maximum recovery if oil is permitted to move away from his property and be produced from the wells of a neighbor's lease. Migration is an operating difficulty easily overlooked in an operator's concern with the many day-to-day problems requiring his attention. Fluids can move within the reservoir rock from high to low pressure areas whenever the two areas are connected through the reservoir. These fluids will move without respect to surface lease lines, the amount of movement governed only by the pressure differential and the ease with which the fluids can move through connecting pore spaces of the rock. Under the rules of capture a property owner or an operator does not own the oil under his property until he has reduced it to possession, so attention to possible migration is of importance.

Causes of Migration

Pressure differential is the basic condition that permits migration of oil from one area to another (Fig. 121A). Two possible ways in which the pressure differential condition might be created are illustrated in Views B and C of Fig. 121. The first way is under-development of Lease Y and the second is lack of full participation in current allowables by the operator of Lease Y. This may occur as a result of allowable penalty or as a result of poorly completed wells causing low productivity. In both ways migration loss from Lease Y results from lack of equitable oil production based on the amount of oil occurring under each operator's property.

Both operators, as shown in Fig. 121C, have drilled equal-sized leases to the same well density. Each lease has 16 wells; however, wells on Lease X are producing the field top per-well allowable of 100 barrels per day per well. Wells on Lease Y average only 50 barrels per day per well, or a total of 800 barrels per day for the 16 wells. With 1,600 barrels per day withdrawals on the Lease X and only 800 barrels per day on Lease Y, a pressure gradient will be formed in the continuous, permeable sand causing migration of oil from Y to X. Migration, caused by development pattern, time of development or by failure to maintain wells at top allowable for the field, is an ever-present possibility commencing with discovery and ending only with abandonment of the field.

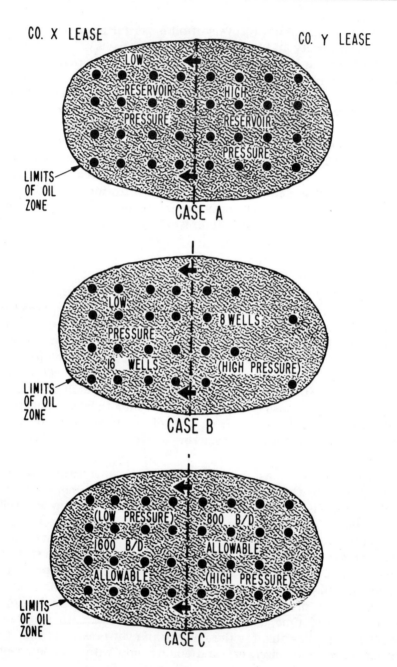

CO. X LEASE
CO. Y LEASE

LOW
RESERVOIR
PRESSURE
HIGH
RESERVOIR
PRESSURE

LIMITS
OF OIL
ZONE

CASE A

LOW
PRESSURE
16 WELLS
8 WELLS
(HIGH PRESSURE)

LIMITS
OF OIL
ZONE

CASE B

(LOW PRESSURE)
1600 B/D
ALLOWABLE
800 B/D
ALLOWABLE
(HIGH PRESSURE)

LIMITS
OF OIL
ZONE

CASE C

Fig. 121—*Field indications of migration.*

Migration Caused by Drives

Migration can also be caused by the natural drives under which the field is being produced. Operators in fields with water drive or gas cap drive mechanisms must recognize these effects in order to tailor operating programs, insofar as permitted or directed by existing regulations or other conditions, for equitable participation in ultimate recovery. For example, in a gas cap drive reservoir where operators are conserving the gas, as shown in Fig. 122A, oil will be moved downstructure from Lease X to Lease Y by the expanding gas cap. Therefore, Operator X will not get all of the otherwise recoverable oil originally in place under his lease. Operator Y would get more than the recoverable oil originally in place under his property, simply because of his favorable downstructure location in the gas cap drive reservoir. Also, Operator Y will end up with gas that has migrated by the drive across the lease line to his property.

Knowing this condition will exist, even though both operators have taken care to conserve natural energy, Operator X should be more concerned about his daily allowables. If he does not get the oil each day under existing allowable schedules, withdrawals from downstructure will cause the gas cap to expand through his property and flush oil to the downdip operator. By keeping

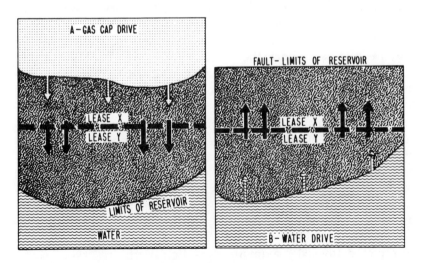

Fig. 122—*Oil migration caused by drives.*

each well producing at top allowable, Operator X can minimize his loss by natural drive migration and get as large a part of his oil as possible before being flooded out by the expanding gas cap.

Operator Y can also improve his ultimate participation by maintaining his wells at top allowable until the gas cap expands onto the edge of his lease. By doing this, he will continue to pull oil zone pressure down as much as permitted under the operating rules and thereby hasten gas-cap expansion to his lease line. If he lets his wells become incapable of producing their allowables, withdrawals and pressure decline will not be as great. He will therefore permit slower gas-cap expansion, giving Operator X more time to produce the wells and gain in more total production.

The effect of water drive is illustrated in Fig. 122B. In this case, the position of the two operators is reversed. Operator Y must maintain participation by keeping his allowables up on a day-by-day basis or lose in ultimate participation. Operator X must also protect his position until the water front reaches his lease line or he will lose in ultimate production.

The two examples quoted are very generalized and would apply strictly only if the reservoir is composed of a single, uniform bed. Stratification of the producing zone will complicate the problem of migration possibilities. In addition, if a combination drive exists, the migration problem may be very complex. The drive itself may change from gas cap to water or vice versa if production rates are changed; therefore, the migration problem may be reversed under the different rates. It also may be possible for reservoir migrations to compensate, with one strata producing under gas-cap expansion and another strata producing principally by water influx.

Individual operators attempting to produce maximum percentages of oil often damage reservoirs as a whole, causing low over-all recovery efficiency, and indeed even causing possible decrease in their own recoverable reserve. Natural migration will occur, depending upon drive mechanism and/or operating practices, to an extent which will be at least partially controllable by prudent operations. Careful study of the field, its drive mechanism and the individual operator's competitive position in it should be directed toward maximum utilization of the reservor energy and equitable participation. Cooperation between operators in a concerted attempt to increase recovery from the reservoir as a whole seldom results in a program which does not provide more oil and economic advantage for each individual operator concerned than he could obtain under competitive operations.

Gas-Cap Shrinkage

Under certain conditions of field operations, gas is produced directly from the gas cap. If this production exceeds the amount that would have entered the oil zone as a result of expansion from pressure drop occurring during production operations, the gas-cap gas will not advance as a driving force under gas-cap expansion. Instead, the gas cap will shrink in volume with oil moving into the pore space that was originally the gas cap. When this occurs recovery from the oil zone is less efficient than for even the least efficient type of drive—the dissolved gas drive.

Under original reservoir conditions, there is a connate-water saturation within the gas cap (Fig. 123A), although it is usually lower than that in the oil zone. When oil moves into the gas cap as a result of gas-cap gas production (Fig. 123B), the oil tends to fill the pore spaces in preference to gas. Even though there is a film of water present, the oil tends to wet the rock. Part of this oil is held in the pore spaces by capillary forces even though the gas cap may later be expanded back, through the pore spaces originally occupied by gas (Fig. 123C). Thus some oil that moved into the gas cap will have been retained on the sand grains and in the pore channels within the original gas-cap area. The bulk of this oil thereafter is not recoverable by present known methods.

Illustrating the problem in dollars and cents emphasizes its full significance. For example, if reservoir pressure is at about 2,500 pounds per square inch, 1 barrel of oil will occupy the space of about 1,000 standard cubic feet of gas in the reservoir. Even if gas is being sold, the oil lost into the cap is equivalent to, say, $2.75 per barrel. On the other hand, the 1,000 cubic feet of gas which was produced and sold may only bring on the order of $0.10. Obviously the sale of excess free gas does not approach compensating the loss in oil recovery.

Gas-cap shrinkage can occur if a pure gas cap drive is present;

however, if some water drive also occurs, gas-cap shrinkage can inadvertently occur more easily. This is caused by the water drive tending to maintain pressure and push the oil ahead into the gas cap as gas is produced from the gas cap (Fig. 124). The factors that are highly conducive to gas-cap shrinkage, therefore, are (1) wells near the gas cap producing with high gas-oil ratios, (2) a water drive present as indicated by water production in wells low on the structure and (3) bottom-hole pressure in oil wells being maintained. It is extremely important to recognize that high gas-oil ratio wells may continue as such and still have oil migrating into the cap between wells. This is caused by the persistent nature of gas cones and fingers created at the high-ratio wells, by high-pressure gradients and by the very nature of the radial flow mechanism.

Methods to correct gas-cap shrinkage involve maintaining the gas cap in the expanded conditions. Such methods are elimination of gas-cap gas production by (1) shutting in high gas-oil ratio producing wells, (2) transferring allowables of high gas-oil ratio wells to low-ratio wells and (3) otherwise reducing free gas production by such means as drastically curtailing allowables. If prevention of further gas production will not correct the shrinking conditions, then it may be necessary to inject gas into the gas cap if economics warrant it. Another more costly means of

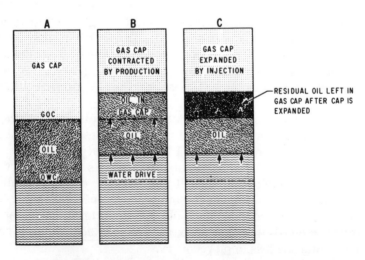

Fig. 123—*Oil lost in gas cap by gas-cap shrinkage.*

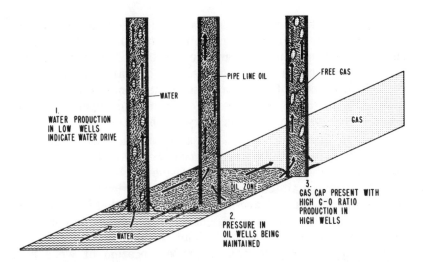

Fig. 124—*Pressure and production trends associated with gas-cap shrinkage.*

correcting the situation would be to produce large quantities of water to prevent the water from entering the reservoir at high rates or to reduce the effectiveness of the water drive. Also, higher rates of oil production may help for a while, but usually only lead to more intensified shrinkage of the gas cap at some later date because the basic trouble results from having removed too much gas from the cap.

In reservoirs with thin oil columns, it may be impossible to control effectively the gas-oil ratios because workovers and allowable transfers may be of no benefit if most of the wells produce substantial quantities of free gas. Under such conditions, it is probable that the most practical means for correcting gas-cap shrinkage will be by injection of gas into the gas cap of the reservoir. Whether such an operation is feasible may be primarily an economic question because of the high cost of injection facilities.

Pressure Maintenance

Carefully controlled production of oil from reservoirs with effective water drives and large gas caps will generally yield a greater return of both oil and profits than haphazard and inefficient production methods. If weak water or gas cap drives result from low reservoir permeability, the operator may maintain reservoir pressure to some degree by reducing production rates or by stringent control of free gas or water production. If careful control cannot be accomplished, supplementing the inadequate natural drives by pressure maintenance operations will generally lead to greater oil recovery and profits.

Pressure maintenance is the augmentation of inadequate natural drives by gas or water injection, before reservoir pressure drops appreciably, to maintain oil displacing energy at a high level. Pressure maintenance operations, particularly those involving injection of gas, are not necessarily limited to augmentation of natural energy; they may assist in the correction of reservoir behavior problems brought about through improper well location and poor completions. Improper location of wells may cause gas-cap shrinkage or early channeling of gas or water to the wells, and poor completions may cause loss of oil to a thief sand open in the interval or by channeling along poor cement jobs.

The chief advantages of pressure maintenance operations are to force gas or water through the reservoir oil zone and physically force oil out of the pore spaces and into the wellbores. This can assist displacement drives already present and replace natural dissolved gas drive. Other advantages are those assisting the displacement process, such as keeping the oil in the gas-saturated state, keeping the viscosity of oil low so that it can move easier and keeping pressure high so oil will flow easily to the wells to result in higher productivity.

Secondary Recovery

For many reasons, a reservoir may approach the end of its primary life having recovered only a small fraction of the oil in place. These reasons include such things as: (1) discovery and production of the reservoir prior to knowledge of good development and production practices; (2) unknown or nonpreventable occurrences such as a casing leak, dissipating reservoir energy; (3) unwillingness of operator to invest further capital while wells are producing at economically attractive rates; (4) need for expensive production practices to obtain maximum recovery shortly after development costs, deferring return on investment beyond primary life; and (5) failure of operator to recognize advantages of early reservoir planning and operational control. Occurrence of these or other problems may make secondary recovery operations feasible and economically attractive at some later date. Secondary recovery operations are defined as those operations wherein depleted or nearly depleted reservoirs are rejuvenated. Usually, such operations include the application of a man-made drive by low pressure gas or waterflood projects.

Although secondary recovery operations in many cases are very attractive economically, the degree to which they are attractive depends upon the efficiency with which the reservoir was produced originally. Dissolved gas drive is the most inefficient type of primary reservoir drive, and therefore, the most logical reservoir on which to apply secondary recovery operations. Under current economic conditions, carefully controlled production of reservoirs during primary stages usually will yield greater over-all return of both oil and profits than can be obtained

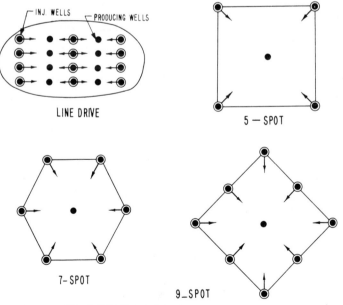

Fig. 125—*Secondary recovery patterns.*

by inefficient primary production methods followed by conventional secondary recovery operations. This careful control of primary production entails taking maximum advantage of natural water or gas cap drives and supplementing some artificial drive to augment inadequate drives.

Conventional secondary recovery operations involve injection of large quantities of water or gas to move through the reservoir and displace additional oil to the wellbores where it can be recovered. Just as water drive is usually more efficient than gas cap drive in displacing oil under natural forces, so water flood is usually more efficient than low-pressure gas drive under secondary operations for the same reasons.

Injection Patterns

A number of types of water floods and gas drives are classified in general relation to the spacing or pattern used to inject the water or gas. These types are the line drive, 5-spot, 7-spot, and 9-spot (Fig. 125) and the irregular pattern. In addition, a common pattern is the peripheral pattern in which wells around the periphery of the field or lease are used for injection purposes. The type of injection pattern many times is controlled by such factors as location of existing wells, nature of offset operations, geometry of the reservoir in question and cost of drilling new wells.

A line drive operation is one in which injection wells are located in a row. There may be only one line of injection wells, located low on the structure for water flooding or high on the structure for gas drive. On the other hand, they may be located as alternate rows of producing and injection wells. The important feature of any spot pattern is to trap oil inside a pattern of injection wells and drive it to a producing well. To illustrate the nature of secondary recovery operations, a 5-spot waterflood project will be discussed in more detail in the following paragraphs.

The 5-Spot Pattern

Operating histories of successful waterflood projects usually are similar in nature. A description of the displacement mechanism occurring under a 5-spot pattern will indicate the nature of other secondary recovery operations. The 5-spot pattern uses a producing well having injection wells one location distant in four directions; thus, four injection wells drive oil inward to the centrally located producing well. If only one 5-spot exists, investment will naturally be high, the ratio of injection to producing wells being 4:1; however, the usual secondary recovery operation is large enough to permit a number of adjacent 5-spots to be included in the project. In such case, the number of injection wells compared to number of producing wells approaches a 1:1 ratio.

WATER FLOOD—STEP 1

At start of operations, with the dissolved gas drive reservoir depleted of pressure, gas saturation throughout the reservoir will usually be 20 to 30 per cent of pore space, with residual oil saturation being about 45 to 55 per cent, depending upon percentage of connate-water saturation (Fig. 126). Fig. 126A shows the map view and Fig. 126B a schematic cross-section of a project 5-spot. Through a four-step sequence of illustrations of the history of a 5-spot performance, the map views illustrate where fluids are located areally in the pattern and the cross-sections show where fluids are located in the sand between the production and injection wells. Gas, oil and water saturations are shown separately and schematically to illustrate magnitude of saturation; however, in the reservoir all three fluids are distributed throughout the reservoir rock. A conventional production rate-time curve is shown in Fig. 127 with the points in the production history of the 5-spot project indicated on the curve.

WATER FLOOD—STEP 2

After the project is initiated and a certain amount of water injected into the reservoir, an area of high water saturation occurs around each injection well. The front of this area of high water saturation is considered to be in the form of a "water bank". Ahead of the water bank for a certain distance, the oil is banked up in a region of high oil saturation. This area is termed either an oil seal or an oil bank. In front of this oil seal and on

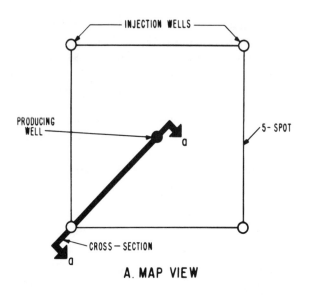

INJECTION WELLS

PRODUCING
WELL

5- SPOT

CROSS — SECTION

A. MAP VIEW

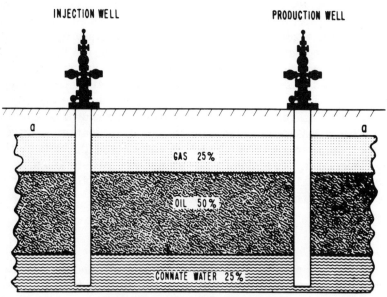

INJECTION WELL

PRODUCTION WELL

a

a

GAS 25%

OIL 50%

CONNATE WATER 25%

B. SCHEMATIC CROSS SECTION

Fig. 126—*Water flood, Step 1—at start of 5-spot operations with uniform reservoir oil, gas and connate-water saturations.*

toward the well, the reservoir is still in a condition similar to that at the beginning of the secondary recovery operation (Fig. 128).

WATER FLOOD—STEP 3

As additional quantities of water are injected, the water bank grows radially and the oil seal grows in area until nearly all gas pore space has been filled with either oil or water. This is called the point of reservoir fill-up because space occupied by gas at the start of the project under low pressure conditions has now been filled with displaced and displacing fluids. At this point oil production begins increasing rapidly (Figs. 127 and 129). A definite pressure reflection is evident in both injection and producing wells if water injection rates are altered in the injection wells. This, of course, occurs because high liquid saturation throughout the reservoir is largely unaffected by the small cushioning effect of the low residual gas saturation. Ease of injecting water into the injection wells decreases as the oil seal and water bank grow until the fill-up point is reached. At this time a back pressure of some magnitude may be required to inject enough water to maintain suitable oil production rates.

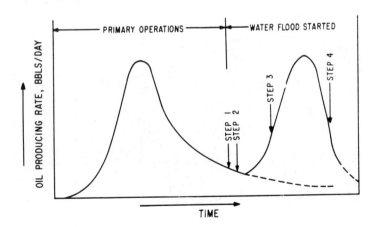

Fig. 127—*Typical primary production history of dissolved gas drive reservoir followed by waterflood operations.*

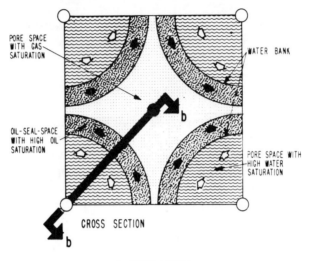

PORE SPACE
WITH GAS
SATURATION

WATER BANK

OIL-SEAL-SPACE
WITH HIGH OIL
SATURATION

PORE SPACE WITH
HIGH WATER
SATURATION

CROSS SECTION

b

A. MAP VIEW

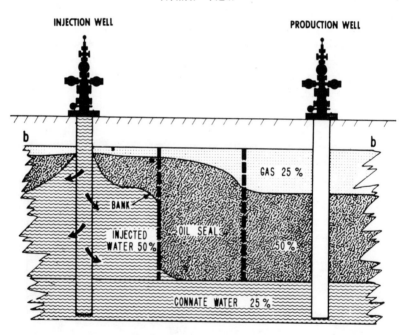

INJECTION WELL

PRODUCTION WELL

b

b

GAS 25 %

BANK

INJECTED
WATER 50 %

OIL SEAL

50 %

CONNATE WATER 25 %

B. SCHEMATIC CROSS SECTION

Fig. 128—*Water flood, Step 2—water bank and oil seal formed in
5-spot operation.*

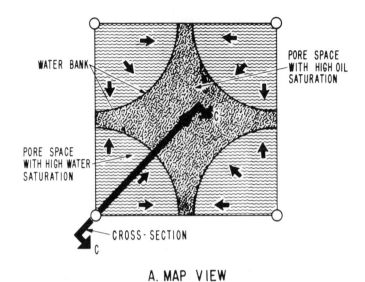

A. MAP VIEW

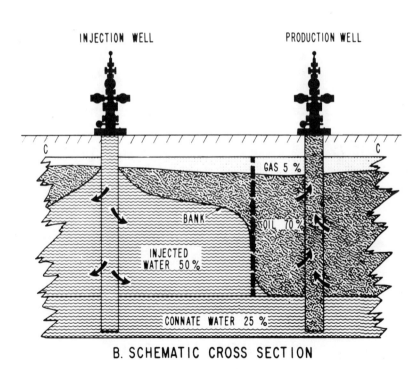

B. SCHEMATIC CROSS SECTION

Fig. 129—*Water flood, Step 3—reservoir at fill-up in 5-spot operation.*

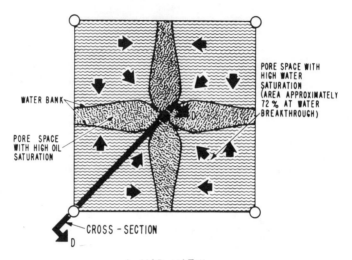

A. MAP VIEW

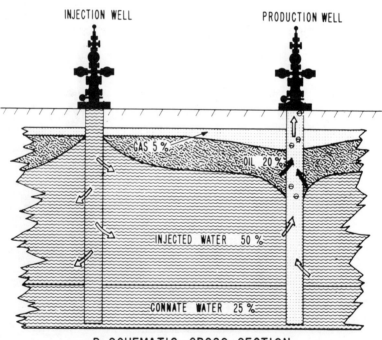

B. SCHEMATIC CROSS SECTION

Fig. 130—*Water flood, Step 4—reservoir near abandonment.*

WATER FLOOD—STEP 4

As the project progresses with either pipe line oil production, or at least low percentages of water production, the time comes when injected water reaches the producing well. The percentage of water production rises rapidly thereafter and oil production percentages and rates drop off. This point is illustrated by Figs. 130 and 127. Ultimate recovery of secondary oil is reached and the project abandoned when oil production rates become insufficient to pay for the additional lifting and handling costs incurred by the high water-production rates.

In essence, the secondary recovery project is merely one in which the operator examines his reservoir after inefficient primary operations, pumps extraneous material such as gas or water through the reservoir pore spaces, leaves some of this material to occupy reservoir space once occupied by oil, and thereby recovers additional quantities of oil from the reservoir. In the case of the secondary recovery project, however, the displacing action

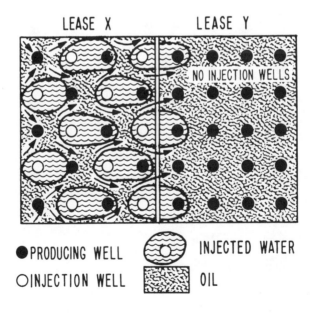

Fig. 131—*Water flood with migration of oil from project across lease line.*

requires that nearly all energy be applied from outside the reservoir; whereas, under best operating conditions, natural energy within the reservoir should be conserved, if practical, and used efficiently to eliminate the costly operations of secondary recovery.

Secondary recovery usually involves rejuvenation of reservoir energy by increase in pressure through either water or gas injection. If secondary recovery operations are carried on with increased pressure over only a portion of the reservoir, oil will migrate away from the project area. This can prove detrimental to the operator of the secondary recovery project. The operator will lose some of the oil originally under his property to an offset operator who does not cooperate with the secondary recovery project by joining into the injection operations. Fig. 131 illustrates a secondary recovery project where migration is occurring across

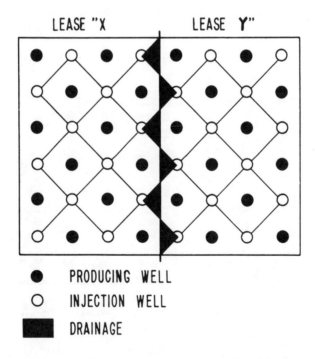

Fig. 132—*Water flood, with compensatory drainage between two offsetting leases.*

a lease line because the offset operator did not inject water at the same time. Fig. 132 illustrates cooperative action by both operators, with migration occurring but in a compensating manner so that, in essence, equities are being protected.

One of the fundamental considerations in properly designing an effective and efficient secondary recovery project is that of providing displacement of oil from the greatest quantity of reservoir pore space possible with economic capital outlay. To accomplish this, thorough knowledge must be obtained of shape and continuity of all producing layers making up the reservoir rock. Few reservoirs are made up of one continuous layer of permeable rock. Fig. 133 illustrates the general reservoir complexity found in practice. The type pattern used, therefore, should be chosen only after reservoir geometry is known. When the complexity of the reservoir is known in detail, injection patterns based on reservoir geometry can usually be set up to provide more oil recovery than that obtainable under an arbitrary 5-spot pattern.

The 5-spot pattern has certain advantages, however: (1) water can be injected rapidly, reducing fill-up time and possibly providing maximum production rates and return on the invest-

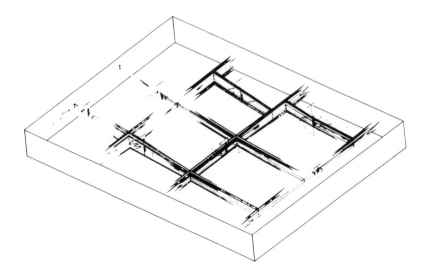

Fig. 133—*Three-dimensional diagram illustrating general reservoir complexity. (Courtesy* Journal of Petroleum Technology—*June, 1958.)*

ment; and (2) water can be put into more reservoir area, allowing operations to be carried out with greater assurance of payout of the investment when insufficient geological and engineering information are available to design the flood properly. Where secondary recovery prospects are apparent, the cost of obtaining enough data through a planned formation evaluation program to properly design the secondary recovery program will usually be small compared to resulting profits.

The most important factors an operator should consider in planning and carrying out a secondary recovery project are: (1) the project should be based on good reservoir data and engineering study; (2) the injection pattern should be consistent with the nature and continuity of the reservoir concerned; (3) the zone to be produced should be thoroughly isolated, especially for water injection; (4) the flood should be kept volumetrically balanced so that water reaches the producing well from various injection wells simultaneously; and (5) full cooperation of offset operators should be secured to prevent migration and obtain equitable compensatory lease drainage.

♦

♦

♦

Profitable and Efficient Rates of Oil Production

Petroleum operators, like people engaged in any other commercial enterprise, are in business for one principal reason—to make a profit. Unlike some other business enterprises, however, the petroleum industry is concerned with utilization of a depleting asset (oil and gas reserves) which are both difficult and expensive to find and develop. As a result, once a reserve is found, the operator must achieve maximum oil and gas recovery consistent with the good business principles common to all enterprises. This means that management must base decisions concerning development and operating programs for a reservoir on economic considerations, as well as on such intrinsic factors as its responsibility to royalty owners, stockholders, employees and the public.

Oil and gas deposits, being depletable natural resources, have a time limited earning capacity which affects their value in a way that usually does not apply to real or industrial property. The capital value of such deposits is depleted within some time period; therefore, rate of return of capital earnings and interest on the capital are prime factors in oil production operations. Greater profit is made at higher producing rates with given amounts of recovery, and the problem resolves itself in obtaining the optimum between maximum recovery and greatest rate.

Proper utilization of the best reservoir drive mechanism and obtaining the best displacement efficiency from that drive mechanism requires that full recognition and proper advantage be taken of the many physical factors governing the productive behavior of the reservoir. Many of these advantages are utilized through such things as proper development, well locations, well completions and subsequent operations. Although these factors have been described in other chapters, the rate factor (being of such great economic importance) will be treated in this chapter in more detail.

Both theory and practical results of reservoir performance have shown repeatedly and clearly that rate of withdrawal of oil will have significant influence on the efficiency of oil recovery in a large number (but not all) of reservoirs. For properly developed reservoirs producing under their primary drive, the trend in most cases is for greater efficiency with rates at something less than wide open flow. However, in many improperly developed reservoirs, the operator may receive considerable benefit from production rate adjustments.

There is no simple formula by which an efficient rate or an optimum rate of production can be established. This has perhaps been the underlying cause in past years for the existence of a great controversy concerning the degree of efficiency attributable to rates. No simple formula is available to determine increments of recovering efficiencies between rates because the physical characteristics of all parts of the reservoir simply cannot be established; also, the reservoir can be produced only once. No one can apply equations and formulas to predict (with any assurance of accuracy) the behavior of a reservoir hundreds of feet from the wellbore if he has no way of obtaining information on the physical characteristics of the formation or its contained fluids in that portion of the reservoir. Therefore, one must rely upon reservoir behavior trends and characteristic factors determined on an extremely small part of the reservoir—that part penetrated while drilling and taken as a core. Results of studies of past and future performance based upon such limited data are subject to so much individual interpretation that variations in interpretation and differences of opinion can affect the thinking of individual operators, particularly when other economic factors are superimposed.

Of as much significance to the problem is the establishment

of criteria for determining the rate of oil production that would lead to efficient production. The real problem is that of defining "efficient production". For a number of years, the petroleum industry has assumed that an optimum rate exists which will give a maximum efficiency in recovery from any given reservoir. This has led to the concept that a range of rates exists, all of which are efficient. Along with this, the concept of "maximum efficient rate", has developed which is considered to be the highest rate within the previously mentioned range of rates.

Because of the great number of situations occurring with various operators that would affect their various definitions within the scope of the efficient rate concept, this book will not attempt to isolate and define any specific category of efficient rates; instead, the general principles will be described from the standpoint of both physics and economics. It should be recognized that a practical rate, in itself, may not directly influence recovery efficiency but may do so indirectly by influencing those various factors that do influence recovery directly.

Reservoir Conditions Which Influence
Efficient Rates of Production

Uniformity of Reservoir Rock

The degree to which the reservoir rock is uniform will influence the rate at which oil can be efficiently displaced from the rock. If the displacing water moves through water-wet reservoir rock at too great a velocity, oil within low permeability lenses, or streaks, will tend to be retained, by-passed by the displacing water, and become economically unrecoverable. At slower rates, water will enter low permeability, water-wet sand by capillary imbibition and will eject oil from the tight sections into the more permeable sections where it can be moved to the well by the water and recovered. If a lens is by-passed, this capillary action will still occur slowly, but the oil ejected will be smeared out behind the displacing water front; its recovery will depend upon the economic feasibility of lifting large quantities of water along with the produced oil. Excessive stratification of the reservoir rock will make the displacing fluids more susceptible to fingering along high permeability streaks to the well at all rates of production, depending to a great extent upon where the well is completed; thus, lower rates may be expected to provide greater recovery efficiency.

Configuration of Pore Space

The size and shape of the pore spaces and the degree of connection between the pore spaces will have an important influence on recovery. More oil will be retained in the smaller pore spaces or even in rocks with larger grain size when the fluid must follow a tortuous path in order to reach the wellbore. In many instances, lower producing rates can minimize the tendency for the displacing fluid to by-pass the smaller and more tortuous pore spaces, thus permitting higher recovery.

Fluid Characteristics

Characteristics of both the oil and the displacing fluid will influence efficient production rates. The higher the viscosity of the oil and the lower the viscosity of the displacing fluid, the lower will be the percentage of oil recovery. Higher oil viscosities tend to retard the rate at which capillary forces can deplete tight sand lenses; therefore, viscosity indirectly affects recovery through the rate factor.

Structure

A high relief structure will permit a greater degree of gravitaional segregation between oil and water and gas and oil than will a low relief structure. Most any rate of production may be quite efficient because of this segregation. Low relief structures may require high rates to cause the oil to be displaced as a bank rather than permitting water to under-ride or gas to over-ride the oil, mix with the oil and result in low displacement efficiency. On the other hand, if water underlies or gas overlies the oil zone, low rates may be required to prevent coning and fingering of gas and water into the well completions which would reduce recovery efficiency.

In a dissolved gas drive or gas cap drive reservoir, wells completed structurally low may sustain higher efficient rates because of the aid of gravity. Operators producing from high on the structure of such reservoirs, however, may attempt to produce at higher rates to compete with other operators. To recover a maximum amount of oil from the over-all reservoir by primary dissolved gas or gas cap drives in reservoirs having high structural relief, the production should be taken from wells located low on the structure and at lower rates.

In a water drive reservoir, structure plays a similar role, although not so pronounced as in other types of drive. For maximum oil recovery by water drive, production should be taken from wells located high on the structure and at lower rates.

Geometry and Pattern

Geometry of the structure may limit the area through which water can enter to displace oil and, thus, influence the rate of water influx. The geometry and nonuniformity of sedimentation may combine to make the pattern of displacement very inefficient. In such cases, not only rate of production but proper adjustment of production rates from individual wells may be required for maximum oil efficiency and recovery.

Size of Reservoir

For any given sand thickness and given well density, the smaller reservoir has a greater periphery per well and can produce at higher well rates for the same linear water advance than can the larger reservoir. However, structural conditions and geometry of the reservoir combine to indirectly influence this. factor.

Influence of Reservoir Drives on Efficient Rates of Production

Predominant Type of Drive

One of the major factors affecting efficient production rate is the type of drive which predominates. The basic difference in the degree of efficiency to be expected from the three principal types of drive has already been discussed. The controlling drive may change from a less efficient to a more efficient one if the rate of production is reduced. A dissolved gas drive may change to gas cap drive by gravitational segregation of gas and oil within the reservoir, or a combination drive may change to water drive if the production rate is reduced and the water is thereby given time to keep up with the oil as pressure drops and the oil moves to the wellbores. It may not always be economically practical, however, to restrict producing rates sufficiently to change the predominant-type drive.

The rate at which oil is produced can make considerable difference in the amount of oil recovered within the scope of each individual type drive. In the case of dissolved gas drive, slower rates may permit an increase in recovery by completely altering the depletion drive to that of a displacement drive. Of course, this is most likely to occur in those dissolved gas drive reservoirs which have high permeability or high structural relief. In gas cap drive reservoirs, the rate of production will affect the uniformity of gas-cap expansion. A loss in efficiency and recovery of oil from the reservoir may be experienced if expansion is not uniform. In the case of a water drive reservoir, excessive withdrawal rates may aggravate by-passing of water around tight sections and low permeability streaks. If the water drive is weak, high rates may even cause a lower efficiency, dissolved gas drive mechanism to predominate. Higher rates also aggravate fingering and coning of a gas-cap gas or bottom water and, thus, may reduce efficiency of production and increase operating costs.

Water Drive

The first objective in achieving efficient performance of a water drive reservoir is to obtain a high displacement efficiency —that is, to maintain an even advance of the water front, to minimize by-passing, to prevent coning or fingering of the invading water and to give the water a chance to eject oil from the tighter sections (by means of capillary forces). Water production in large quantities from individual wells is to be expected before efficient and complete flushing is obtained; however, any indications that wells are producing high volumes of water which do not contribute to the flushing of oil should immediately be investigated. If the water is coning or fingering through a permeable streak, it is quite possible that it is bringing little or no oil into the wellbore; therefore, such water production is undesirable. It does not contribute toward oil recovery or profit, causes an increase in lifting and disposal costs, and represents a waste of reservoir energy.

Water production from water drive reservoirs can have a marked influence on recovery from other reservoirs producing from the same formation and located within a common aquifer. An example of this is the Woodbine basin in East Texas. The resultant effect is that all reservoirs in the basin which produce from the respective formations are influenced to a degree by the withdrawal rate of each other. The smaller reservoirs, however, have less influence on pressure decline of both the basin and the individual reservoir. Recovery from a particular reservoir will probably be closely related to lifting costs, which is in turn related to drop in basin pressure. The larger reservoirs, having the major influence on basin pressure, also exert the major influence on recovery both for themselves and for the smaller reservoirs. Where there are basin effects caused by having a common aquifer, therefore, efficient rates between reservoirs may be related.

Gas Cap Drive

The most important objective in a gas cap drive reservoir is to retain the gas-cap gas in the reservoir in order to maintain reservoir energy and promote high oil displacement efficiency. To this end, most oil should be produced from low ratio wells. Where wells are prorated, the allowables of high ratio wells are transferred to low ratio wells. High gas-oil ratio wells sometimes are voluntarily shut in to prevent production of gas-cap gas. By keeping the gas in the cap, reservoir pressure will be maintained better, solution gas will be retained in the reservoir oil and oil viscosity will be kept low. Higher production rates may be effected without gas fingering (which lowers recovery efficiency) if a uniform pressure distribution is maintained in the gas cap. Much higher recoveries can be obtained in gas cap drive reservoirs if there is sufficient structural relief to permit appreciable gravitational segregation of the oil downstructure to the producing wells; higher structural relief permits higher rates compared to reservoirs with lower structural relief. Producing rates for new gas cap drive reservoirs, however, are usuaally no higher than water drive reservoirs of comparable size.

Dissolved Gas Drive

If gravity is neglected, producing rate probably has little effect on ultimate recovery from dissolved gas drive reservoirs; however, gravity does have some effect in most reservoirs because some structural relief is usually present. Therefore, slower producing rates are desirable for dissolved gas drive conditions to permit more gravitational segregation and, if economically practical, to allow one of the more efficient displacement mechanisms to form as the predominant or supplementary drive.

Stripper Fields

When a reservoir has reached the stripper category, with greater than three-fourths of the primary recoverable oil already produced, it is probable that a change in rate will not significantly alter the ultimate recovery. On this basis, capacity production becomes the practical rate because of pronounced economic considerations.

Secondary Recovery Operations

There is great room in secondary recovery operations for controversy regarding the effect of production rate on recovery efficiency. Actually, some different conditions are present under secondary operations as compared to primary operations, and different factors prevail. Under secondary operations the reservoir pressure usually is lower, gas saturation is higher and viscosity of the oil is higher. The source of energy to drive oil to the producing wells is different, being derived from man-made sources. Fluids such as gas or water are injected into single points in the reservoir. Primary operations, on the other hand, find the reservoir pressure higher and energy to produce the oil contained within the oil or located in water or gas zones which occur over a large area of the reservoir as a front.

Under primary operations with pressure high, adequate pressure sinks can be established at the producing wells to cause the oil to move into the wellbores from all directions and, thus, be captured and produced. Oil located near the well has less chance to migrate as a result of saturation variations in the reservoir because low gas saturation occurs throughout the reservoir and does not permit such migration to occur easily.

Under secondary recovery operations, however, oil must move to fill up the pore channels occupied by gas. Oil can move away from the area of influence covered by the wells and be lost in the feather edges of the reservoir outside the influence of the wells. A pressure build-up in the area of the injection wells is necessary to move the oil to the producing wells. The producing wells must have as great a pressure sink as possible to enlarge the area of influence of the producing wells and to assure trapping the oil before it moves outside the pattern area. To have a high pressure sink requires higher rates of production and automatically higher rates of injection.

For a given rate of water advance in the displacing action, a water injection, secondary recovery program in a reservoir can achieve a much higher reservoir production rate than in a water drive reservoir under primary operations. This is because the area of the displacing fluid front in the secondary recovery project may be much greater than in the natural drive project because of the dispersed fluid injection pattern. The best production rate to apply to a secondary recovery project may, therefore, be much greater because of both recovery and economics than the best rate to apply to a primary recovery project. There is no general relation, however, that can be depended upon as a criterion upon which to base such a rate for a given field. Such must be done only after examining all the factors involved, including economics.

**Determination of Efficient
Rates of Production**

Reservoir Study

Although there is no simple formula by which an efficient

rate can be calculated, there are adequate technical bases upon which a determination of the efficient production rate of a reservoir may be made. It is necessary, however, to study all of the factors governing reservoir behavior. Two questions must be answered in arriving at an efficient rate. How fast can the reservoir produce without causing appreciable reduction in ultimate recovery? How fast can the individual wells produce without causing appreciable reduction in ultimate recovery? Both the wells and the reservoir must be studied to determine which should control production operations.

Examination of Pressure-Production Trends

An examination of the pressure-production data trends may often supply the key to the desirable production rate. The influence of the rate on reservoir production, reservoir pressure, water production rate or gas-oil ratio may indicate inefficiency.

Examination of Well Behavior Trends

The effect of producing rate on water or free gas production of the individual well can be determined by examining the production history of the well. Pressure histories of the individual wells are sometimes helpful in indicating producing efficiency. A comparison of water production trends or gas-oil ratio trends with structural relationship is usually desirable for estimating the efficiency of reservoir drive mechanisms. Various methods are used to study these trends. They can be plotted on the basis of individual wells, or groups of wells, or on the basis of structural location with respect to oil-water and gas-oil contact.

Gas-Cap Behavior

Plotting a series of gas-oil ratio maps at various times during the producing life of the reservoir is a method for illustrating gas-cap behavior. An even and regular advance of the gas front is desirable, and failure of the front to advance with pressure drop usually arouses suspicions of gas-cap shrinkage which in itself may result in extreme waste.

Lease Operations
Of Oil Reservoirs

Almost without exception, oil production is attended by gas that comes from solution in the oil at reservoir conditions. This gas, when liberated from solution in the oil, causes the oil to shrink in volume. The term "shrinkage factor" is given to the ratio of the amount of oil recovered in the stock tank from one unit volume of produced reservoir oil. The greater the amount of gas evolving from the oil, the greater will be the shrinkage of the oil and the smaller will be the volume of saleable oil at the surface from a given volume of produced reservoir oil. Both the amount of gas which a given reservoir oil will liberate and the resulting shrinkage factor will depend upon the composition of the reservoir oil and the temperature and pressure under which the oil and gas exist at separation.

Field practices for separating oil and gas mixtures have undergone considerable change in the past 30 years as more knowledge has been gained regarding the manner in which various oil and gas mixtures behave with changes in temperature and pressure. In many cases in the past, operators either flowed wells directly to a stock tank or passed well fluids through a separator operated at just enough pressure to push the oil to the tanks. In those fields which employed gasoline plant operations, lease separators were operated at pressures convenient to plant operations. Quite often little thought was given to the effect surface separation conditions had on recovery of oil in the stock tank. Because more is known now concerning the behavior of oil and gas mixtures, more careful study is being given to each reservoir oil to assure that proper separation and handling techniques are employed in the field to provide the operator with maximum profit from sale of the produced oil and gas.

Differential and Flash Separation

To best explain the various separation processes, it is convenient to consider the component hydrocarbons as "lights", "intermediates" and "heavies". The lights are methane and ethane; the intermediates include propane through hexane; and the heavies are heptane and heavier components. Mechanically, there are two types (or methods) of gas-oil separation—"differential" separation and "flash" or "equilibrium" separation. The light components may be removed little by little from the remaining oil mixture as pressure on the oil is reduced; this is differential separation. If the gas is separated in this manner, a maximum

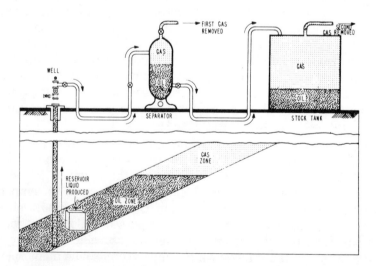

Fig. 134—*Single-stage separation system (one separator). (Courtesy* WORLD OIL—*June, 1951.)*

amount of heavy and intermediate components will remain in the liquid and minimum shrinkage will result. This occurs because gas liberated earlier at higher pressures is not present at lower pressures to attract the intermediates and heavies and pull them into the gas phase in excessive quantities. Flash, or equilibrium separation, is accomplished by keeping all liberated gas in contact with the liquid until its instantaneous removal at the final separation pressure. A maximum proportion of intermediate and heavy components are attracted into the gas phase by this process and result in maximum oil shrinkage. Less oil shrinkage and, thus, greater stock tank oil recovery will normally occur by differential separation processes than will occur by flash separation.

Single-Stage Separation

It can be seen from the foregoing that the best mechanical separation system for retaining absolute maximum recovery of stock tank liquid would be one which would include a large number of separators. In such a system, the oil would be produced to a separator set at the highest possible producible pressure. The separator liquid obtained therein would be passed to successively lower pressure separators until the remaining liquid finally would emerge from a very low pressure separator into the stock tank. This would result in maximum oil recovery because such a procedure would approach the differential liberation process. Quite obviously, such a large separation system would require an extremely high investment, and for that reason, it is impractical. In practice, however, with most average shrinkage oils, only one separator is utilized in the system. Such a system is termed "single-stage separation" (Fig. 134). Single-stage separation of low shrinkage oils generally will recover an amount of oil very near to that which might be expected under conditions of many stages of separation.

In a single-stage separation system, the gas is removed in two batches from the original liquid as pressure drops. The first batch of gas is removed in the separator and the second in the stock tank. By removing some gas in a separator the quantity of intermediate and heavy components attracted to the lights of the gas are minimized and final oil shrinkage is lessened so that more oil is retained in the tank from a given amount of reservoir oil.

It has been found that separator pressure can be adjusted to some particular point which will result in less shrinkage to the oil than would occur at other separator pressures. If separator pressure is set high, a small amount of gas will be removed in the first step at the separator, and a large amount will be removed in the second step at the stock tank. Large quantities of intermediates and heavier components will be lost from the liquid to gas in the stock tank where a large quantity of gas is removed as a second "batch"; therefore, high shrinkage with low stock tank oil recovery will be obtained. If the separator pressure is set very low, a large amount of gas will be separated in the first step at the separator, with a small amount of gas being separated in the second step from the stock tank. Here again, large quantities of intermediates and heavier components will be lost from the liquid to the gas in the separator where a large quantity of gas is removed as a first batch; therefore, high shrinkage with low stock tank oil recovery again will result. On the other hand, if the separator pressure is adjusted to more properly balance the amounts of gas removed.at the separator and at the stock tank, a minimum of intermediates and heavier components will be lost from the liquid to the gas; therefore, lowest shrinkage will occur to the oil and the highest stock tank oil recovery will be obtained from a particular reservoir liquid. The separator pressure found to accomplish this is termed "optimum separator pressure" (Fig. 135).

Two-Stage Separation

Some reservoir oils are classified high shrinkage oils. Although this classification is arbitrary, these oils have higher shrinkage than usual because in the original mixture there are greater quantities of lighter or intermediate components present which vaporize to a greater extent when pressure on the mixture is lowered. Therefore, it may be desirable to employ two separators in the system to obtain optimum economic separation. Such a system is known as "two-stage separation" (Fig. 136). In the case of high shrinkage oil, the two stages of separation merely permit the gas to be removed at three points—first in the high pressure separator, second in the low pressure separator and third in the stock tank. With the gas divided into three batches, there is less tendency for these smaller amounts, separated under their respective conditions of temperature and pressure, to attract and remove the intermediate and heavier (and more valuable) components from the liquid.

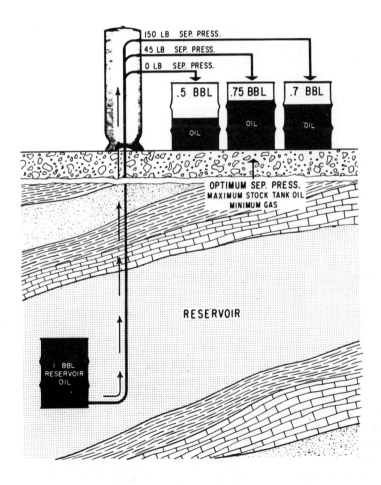

Fig. 135—*Optimum single-stage oil separation for a given oil.*

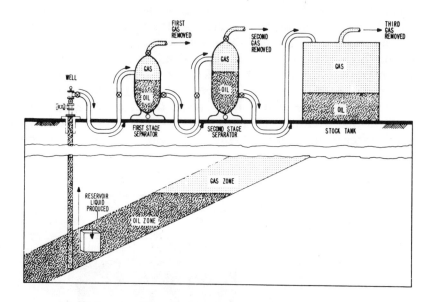

Fig. 136—*Two-stage separation system (two separators).*

In this system, there are optimum pressure conditions for both high and low pressure separators just as there are for the one separator system.

Relationship of Gasoline Plants in Separation

It is not always economical to separate oil and gas by optimum separation. In many cases (for example, in high shrinkage oils and especially for oils where large reserves are concerned), it may be most economical to produce the separated gas to a gasoline plant and remove the last remaining quantities of intermediate and heavy materials in the form of natural gasoline (even after considerable investment for gasoline plant equipment has been made). If such is true, it may be economically justifiable to operate the separators under vacuum conditions to further vaporize intermediate and heavy materials into the gas separated at the separator. This results in removing from the liquid at the separator a maximum amount of intermedi-

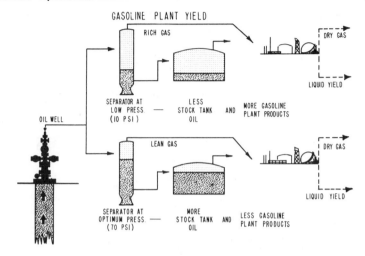

Fig. 137—*Separation and gasoline plant yield.*

ate and heavier components which would be passed as gas to the gasoline plant, providing higher volumes of gasoline plant products.

Economic Summary

The over-all economic problem involving oil and gas separation is summarized in Fig. 137 which schematically shows a producing well connected to two types of separation systems—one to an optimum and the other to a low pressure separator. In the case of optimum separation, maximum oil will be recovered in the stock tank; less intermediate and heavier components will be produced to the gasoline plant; and plant product yield will be small. In the case of the low pressure separation system, a minimum of stock tank oil will be recovered in the stock tank; more intermediate and heavier components will be produced to the gasoline plant; and plant product yield will be large. Therefore, the over-all economics of a project would include such factors as prices of gasoline plant products and stock tank oil, cost of investment in gasoline plant equipment and separators, degree of oil shrinkage, analysis of separated gas, availability and uniformity of markets, and size of oil and gas reserves.

◆

◆

◆

Producing Characteristics Of Gas Wells

Gas wells produce from free gas deposits that are either associated or non-associated with oil accumulations (Fig. 138). Literally, a gas well is one which does not produce oil; however, many oil wells may produce with such high gas-oil ratios that they are classified for commercial or other practical purposes as gas wells.

Casinghead gas, or associated gas, is gas produced along with oil. Some of it may come from gas initially dissolved in the reservoir oil, while some may have moved into the well along with the oil from a gas cap or a free gas zone as a result of completion or producing practices.

It was shown in Chapter 8 that production of associated gas from a gas cap can materially decrease oil recovery by causing shrinkage of the gas-cap volume, permitting oil movement into the gas cap. Once oil has moved into a gas cap, large quantities are absorbed and retained by the dry grains of the gas sand. Much of this oil cannot be recovered by known methods and must be considered lost. The value of oil lost to the gas cap usually far outweighs that of the in-place gas it replaces. Therefore, it usually is economically unprofitable to produce this gas for current sale alone—unless, of course, no alternative is available to the operator.

Bona fide gas wells do produce from gas caps of oil-producing reservoirs; however, this chapter will discuss only gas wells producing from free gas reservoirs, their fundamental producing characteristics and some of the more common problems they normally present.

As with oil wells, gas well production characteristics principally are reflections of the nature of the individual gas reservoirs. The main oilwell production characteristics include pressure, high gas-oil ratio production and water production trends. The principal gas well production characteristics parallel those of oil wells and include pressure, condensate production and water production trends.

Pressure Trends

Reservoir pressure is a controlling factor in the ability of a well to produce, and decrease in bottom-hole pressure of a gas well will be indicated by a drop in its productivity (Fig. 139).

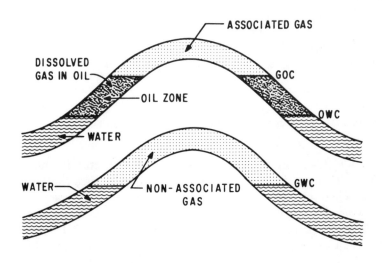

Fig. 138—*Classification of gas based on source in reservoir.*

There are several reasons for the way bottom-hole pressure drops in gas wells. For a given production rate, pressure will decline much faster in small reservoirs than in large ones. Just as with oil reservoirs, however, water influx into the gas reservoir from water-bearing sand outside the original gas zone can help support reservoir pressure in the gas zone. A gas reservoir underlain by large connecting volumes of water would be expected to produce at higher gas rates because the water will expand into the reservoir and maintain pressure under a natural water drive. Water influx in many reservoirs, however, may not be sufficient to sustain pressure and production rates at desired levels.

An extremely rapid bottom-hole pressure drop is sometimes caused by low sand permeability either throughout the reservoir or immediately surrounding the wellbore (Figs. 76 and 77). This same problem may result from reductions in permeability caused during drilling, workover or production operations. Fresh water condensation from the gas due to pressure and temperature reductions near the wellbore may cause reduction in permeability. Bentonitic cementing materials present in sands around the wellbore may swell, if contacted by fresh or brackish water, and create restrictions in the rock pore spaces until permeability of .the sand to the flow of gas is materially reduced near the wellbore. Water blocking around the wellbore by fresh or connate water can be another cause of permeability reduction, again causing a reduction in the pore channels to the point where permeability to gas is significantly restricted.

Condensate Production Trends

While reservoir pressure is a controlling factor in the ability of a well to produce, it also may be a controlling factor in the liquid yield of the produced gas for a given condensate gas reservoir. Liquid yield in the produced gas from such reservoirs tends to decrease as pressure drops (Figs. 139 and 140). This is true because gas that flows to the well and is produced has lost some heavy hydrocarbon components by retrograde condensation in the reservoir rock before arriving at the wellbore (Chapter 3).

While normal condensate gas reservoir production is attended by decreasing liquid yield as reservoir pressure declines, decreased producing pressures are not always accompanied by the lower liquid ratios. Indeed, the occurrence of markedly decreased

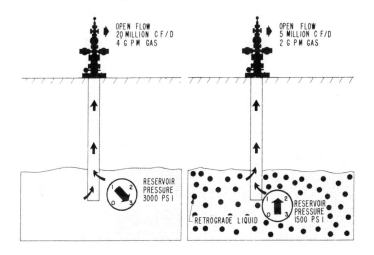

Fig. 139—*Effect of pressure on gas well open-flow capacity and gallons per thousand (GPM) content of produced gas. (Courtesy* WORLD OIL.—*June, 1951.)*

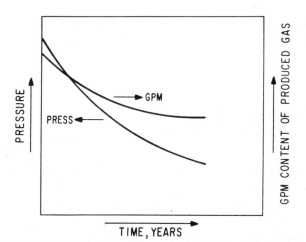

Fig. 140—*Reduction in condensate yield from a well producing from a reservoir with declining pressure.*

producing pressures and rates with a constant liquid ratio may result from mechanical problems at the wellbore itself. Accumulation of either condensed water or hydrocarbon liquids in the sand around the wellbore may cause permeability blocks which can reduce gas flow and producing pressures to very low levels while reservoir pressure, beyond the water or condensate block, remains high. Effective treatment to remove the block will restore normal productivity to the well.

Water Production Trends

Production of water from a gas well can cause permeability reduction. This results either from accumulation of water condensed near the wellbore from the gas as its pressure and temperature decrease or by natural water influx.

Proximity of the gas well's completion interval to the gas-water contact in the reservoir can have quite an influence on optimum production rates. For example, if gas is underlain by water and if a well is completed near the water level, high gas production rates will tend to cone water into the well. This not only wastes reservoir energy, but also may result in a serious reduction in the well's gas deliverability through reduction in the sand's relative permeability to gas and reduced surface flowing pressures caused by having to lift volumes of water. At this point in the reservoir, permeability reduction is most critical to well productivity (Fig. 77).

Precautions and Remedies for
Gas Well Completion Problems

Certain precautions and remedies can be used effectively to prevent or remedy problems of gas well completions. Proper drilling practices may be utilized to prevent reduction of permeability surrounding the wellbore. Some swelling of clays near the well is caused by influx of fresh water filtrate from drilling fluids during drilling or workover operations. To avoid or reduce this swelling, drilling fluid other than fresh water mud is usually employed. Once the problem exists, however, the sand face can be backwashed with acid, or other chemicals can be injected into the reservoir to shrink the clays and increase permeability. Purging the well can sometimes be helpful in removing free water standing in the tubing, which may be a source of trouble.

Fracturing procedures are often used to increase effective permeability surrounding a wellbore. Coning of bottom water into a wellbore may be minimized by employing high completion intervals where reservoir rock permeability is not broken vertically by stratification. Where coning is a problem, however, production rates may be adjusted downward to help prevent cones from forming.

Occasionally, water sands occur as stringers within the gas-bearing sand section, and difficulty is encountered in effecting water shut-off from the water-bearing stringers. It may be most economical in such cases to produce the water along with gas, separate it and dispose of it at the surface, and deplete the parasitic water sand. Other serious problems may occur in the gas-producing zones with the water present, such as clay swelling or water blocking, which may require expensive well workovers. Therefore, well completion and production practices are selected by comparing the economics of the various choices at hand.

Gas Measurements

Gas is composed of molecules which travel back and forth and occupy a great deal more space than their actual volume. They bump into each other, rebound, bump and rebound from the sides of their container. The myriad of bumps taken together create a push which is the pressure on the container. Frequency of bumping reflects their temperature. If more molecules are added to the confined space, frequency of bumps is greater; a greater net push on the sides of the container results in greater pressure. Also, if the speed at which the molecules fly back and forth is increased such as would occur with increased temperature, the number of bumps on the side in a given time would be greater and there would likewise be an increase in pressure.

Atmospheric pressure obviously is that pressure caused by the atmosphere. At sea level atmospheric pressure is approximately 14.7 pounds per square inch. In gas measurements, gauges are ordinarily used which register zero at atmospheric pressure. Absolute pressure, therefore, is gauge pressure plus atmospheric pressure at the place of measurement.

Temperature, or the intensity of heat, is measured by thermometers, the most common being the Fahrenheit. On this scale the freezing point of water is 32° and the boiling point, 212°. Just as absolute units are dealt with in pressure studies, absolute temperature units necessarily must be used in temperature studies. Absolute zero is 492° below the freezing temperature of water or 460° below zero on the Fahrenheit scale.

If pressure on an ideal gas remains constant, volume varies directly as the absolute temperature; if the volume remains constant, the absolute pressure varies with the absolute temperature. When an ideal gas expands or is compressed at constant temperature, volume varies inversely with absolute pressure.

Gas is measured because, usually, one party is selling it to another party. In addition, however, gas measurements are vital in gas reservoir production and operational control. Since natural gas is highly compressible and since temperatures and pressures control the true quantity represented by a given volume of gas, it is necessary that these conditions always be given to specifically describe a given gas.

Gas sales contracts usually specify the temperature to which gas measurements and sales are to be corrected; however, in some cases temperature corrections are not required by contract. This is true because temperature of the gas at the well does not vary greatly. On large deliveries, however, a small percentage in volumetric error will cause large volume errors and require the extra expense of using a recording thermometer.

Pressure variations over a wide range are the rule rather than the exception in gas measurement. Comparatively small variations in gauge pressure may cause a large difference in gas volume considerations. For this reason, recording gauges are almost always used and the volumes measured are corrected to conditions specified by sales contracts.

A "cubic foot" is the accepted unit of gas measurement. The phrase has no definite meaning, however, unless described in terms of temperature and pressure at which the volume exists. The phrase "cubic feet at standard conditions" has come to be used universally; however, standard conditions can vary depending upon the location and circumstances and should always be defined when used. Usually, standard conditions refer to 60° Farenheit and 14.7 pounds per square inch pressure, or atmospheric pressure at sea level.

Super Compressibility of Natural Gas

When gases are heated, they expand; when cooled, they shrink in volume. Gas volume shrinks when pressure is applied and expands when pressure is reduced. An ideal gas (actually only theoretical) is defined as one that, at constant temperature, will shrink to half its volume if absolute pressure on it is doubled; however, a natural gas like most other gases does not behave exactly in this manner.

Natural gas is more compressible in most pressure ranges encountered than the so-called ideal gas. If pressure is increased 10 times, volume decreases to less than one-tenth its original volume (Fig. 141). This has led to the use of super compressibility factors in determinations of gas volume changes. The use of these factors merely corrects for lack of compliance of the natural gas with ideal gas behavior.

The reason natural gas is more compressible than ideal gas is explained in terms of the physical properties discussed in Chapter 3. An ideal gas, because of its defined characteristics, could have no molecules to occupy space. A natural gas actually consists of many molecules of definite size and shape. At low pressure these molecules are relatively far apart, and at high pressure they are close to each other. Molecules exert an attraction for each other, and the closer the molecules are to each other, the stronger that attraction becomes. At high pressure where the molecules are fairly close together, the additional attracting forces present between molecules act as additional

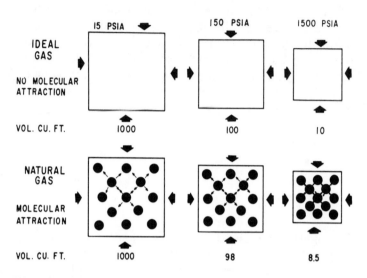

Fig. 141—*Why natural gas is more compressible than ideal gas.*

pressure and cause the gas to occupy a volume less than the ideal ratio dictates (Fig. 141).

At extremely high pressure where molecules are extremely close together, additional forces of molecular repulsion are present. These forces become severe when molecules are so close together that there is an overlap of the electronic fields of atoms making up the molecules. These forces significantly change the magnitude of gas compressibility at pressures greater than 5,000 pounds per square inch and even make the compressibility much less than the ideal gas law would dictate.

Generally, gas purchasers prefer to receive gas at the surface at high pressure and pay on the basis of straight compression ratio, without taking into account the compressibility of the gas. More gas is thereby obtained from a given measured volume.

◆

◆

◆

Gas Reservoirs

The primary difference between a reservoir gas and a reservoir oil is the difference in phase or state in which the material occurs at the existing reservoir pressure and temperature. This difference, however, is caused by a general difference in composition. Reservoir oil is usually a mixture in which heavier hydrocarbon components, normally liquid at atmospheric temperature and pressure, comprise the bulk of the material. On the other hand, reservoir gas is usually a mixture in which the dominant constituents are lighter components.

Natural gas deposits were classified in Chapter 3 as retrograde gas, wet gas and dry gas because of the fundamental differences in their behavior. A variety of conditions may be encountered in gas field operations because of the differences in properties of these gas mixtures; therefore, gas field operations must be planned to cope with the problems of the specific gas being produced.

Retrograde Condensate Gas

Liquid condensation that occurs with pressure decline on a gas is called opposite behavior or "retrograde behavior" because it is the exact reverse of what would normally be expected. Gas exhibiting such behavior is retrograde condensate gas. The intermediate components (propane, butane, pentane and hexane) and heavy components (heptane and heavier), with emphasis on the latter, exhibit retrograde condensation in reservoirs as illustrated in Fig. 142.

A retrograde gas has methane as its major single component, although it is usually rich in intermediate and heavy component content. All materials are in the gaseous state because of the high reservoir pressure and temperature. This is true because at high pressure the molecules composing the mixture are close together, and attractive forces of the light for the heavier components are so high that the heavier components are carried into the gas phase.

Retrograde gas is most commonly encountered in reservoirs deeper than 5,000 feet with pressure exceeding 2,000 pounds per square inch. Condensation of hydrocarbon liquid from this type of gas will take place both in the reservoir and in surface separation equipment. Significant recoveries of condensate can be obtained by any normal surface separation technique. Operating problems associated with retrograde gas production fall into two main categories: (1) obtaining optimum liquid yield from gas produced to the surface and (2) economically preventing loss of liquids by retrograde condensation in the reservoir.

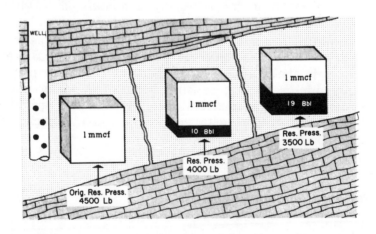

Fig. 142—*Retrograde condensation of liquid from gas in a reservoir.
(Courtesy* WORLD OIL—*June, 1951.)*

Condensate Separation

Just as surface separation techniques of gas and oil mixtures have been altered and improved in the past, so have methods of separating gas and condensate mixtures. Unlike oils, however, these mixtures exist in the reservoir as a gas; when this gas is produced to the surface, it is accompanied by a liquid which has condensed from the gas and is called "condensate". It is important to realize that this condensate was not a liquid in the reservoir, but actually part of the gas. When pressure was lowered on the gas in the reservoir, part of it condensed by retrograde to a liquid and dropped out in the reservoir. But in addition, the temperature drop occurring to the rest of the gas as it then passed on to the surface caused additional liquid condensation at the surface.

The manner in which mixtures of gas and condensate are separated at the surface and temperature and pressure controls are applied influences liquid recovery at the surface much as with crude oil. The principal means of surface separation of gas and condensate has for many years been conventional stage separation. Optimum single-stage separation, as illustrated in Fig. 143, has been popular. In many instances, two-stage separation has been used to increase recovery of condensate over that which would be recovered by single-stage separation.

Single-Stage Separation

An optimum single-stage separation pressure occurs at the surface because of the fundamental behavior of the molecules of the various components of produced condensate and gas. As the two phases (liquid and gas) reach a separator, the liquid has formed because of a combination of (1) expansion of the gas at the lower pressure, which has allowed the heavy and some intermediate component molecules to coalesce through attractive forces, and (2) less molecular activity at the lower temperature, which has further allowed heavy and some intermediate component molecules to coalesce through attractive forces into the liquid phase.

Molecules in the gas mixture are close together at very high separator pressure. Attractive forces between all molecules (heavy, intermediate and light) are sufficiently high that the light molecules retain most heavy and intermediate molecules in the gas phase. A smaller amount of liquid will then form and be produced out of the separator. At low separator pressure, attractive forces of light molecules are much less effective toward holding the heavies in the gas because of the greater distance between the molecules. However, another dispersing force—that of their own kinetic energy—tends to cause the heavy and intermediate molecules to remain in the gas phase. The combination of the attractive forces of light molecules for heavy and intermediate molecules and vaporizing tendencies

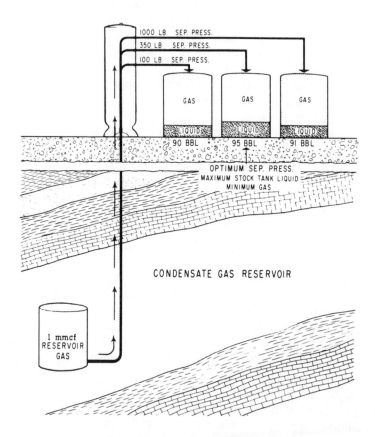

Fig. 143—*Optimum single-stage condensate separation.*
(Courtesy WORLD OIL.—*June, 1951.)*

of heavy and intermediate molecules are both minimized at an in-between or optimum separation pressure. Thus, for a given surface temperature and single-stage separation, a maximum amount of condensate liquid will be recovered with an optimum separator pressure.

Two-Stage Separation

Two-stage separation of gas from condensate at the surface, like the parallel case of two-stage separation of gas from oil at the surface, results in greater recoveries of condensate than will result from single-stage separation. The process works in such a manner that, if maximum liquid is to be obtained, an optimum amount of liquid is formed and removed from the gas in the first stage or high pressure separator at optimum separator pressure. This liquid contains a large amount of light component molecules which must be separated from the liquid at a lower pressure. Like the case of optimum single-stage separation of gas from crude oil, there is an optimum pressure for the second stage or low pressure separator which will allow maximum stock tank liquid to be retained from the liquid separated in the first stage or high pressure condensate gas separator.

Low Temperature Separation

In recent years demand for condensate has increased. As production costs continue to rise, more attention has been focused on developing more efficient and economical field methods of increasing condensate yield from produced gas. Low temperature separators and stabilizers were developed to accomplish this purpose. It long has been known that condensate recovery could be increased over that obtainable by conventional separators by reducing temperature of the produced stream. Actually, some of the first commercial gasoline plants used this method of processing gases before use of absorption-type plants became common practice.

Low temperature separation is much more efficient than conventional separation of the heavy and intermediate components from a gaseous hydrocarbon mixture. Formation of liquids at the surface is primarily caused by drop in temperature of the mixture in moving from the reservoir to the surface. The low temperature method of separation, therefore, is one in which the mixture of gaseous hydrocarbons is subjected to abnormally low temperatures. Temperature effect on condensation of liquids is increased, resulting in more complete condensation of all intermediate and heavy components away from the attractive influence of the light hydrocarbon components. The escaping or vaporizing tendency of the heavier components is reduced by the reduced kinetic energy associated with the temperature drop. In the low temperature separation process, liquids formed in the low temperature equipment are passed to low pressure and higher (atmospheric) temperature separator or storage where the final amounts of light components are changed to gas and separated.

The low temperature separator may be considered a more efficient first stage of a two-stage separation system. It is more efficient because at normal temperatures the great quantity of light components present have great attraction for the normally small quantities of heavier components in the gaseous mixture. Under these conditions, the low temperature is required to force condensation of the heavier components.

As the first-stage unit of a two-stage operation, the low temperature, high pressure separator removes most intermediate and heavy components from the original produced condensate gas mixture. The low temperature conditions in this stage also cause a large quantity of light components to be retained in the liquid. When liquid thus formed passes to the low pressure and high temperature (atmospheric) of the storage tank, the gas liberated from the liquid is composed of not only lights, but also some of the heavier materials. This occurs because attractive forces of the fairly large quantity of light components that leave the liquid carry some of the heavy components into the gas phase. Therefore, another step may be taken to minimize loss through vaporization of heavier components into the gas phase. Liquid from the high pressure, low temperature separator can be very efficiently separated at low pressure and high temperature by a stabilizer column. Heat is applied to the bottom of the stabilizer, and the low temperature separator liquid is passed into the top of the stabilizer. Light components are removed as gas little by little as the mixture is warmed in its route down the column. Gas is removed at the top and liquid at the bottom of the stabilizer. This may be thought of as differential temperature separation where light component molecules are separated gradually as temperature of the mixture increases.

Condensate Yield

Surface yields of condensate from reservoir gas vary from 1 or 2 barrels to as much as 200 barrels or more from a million cubic feet of separated gas, depending upon composition of the reservoir gas. There is no sharp demarcation between dry, wet and retrograde gas. Reservoir gases grade continuously in composition from one extreme to the other without break, into the range of reservoir liquids. The differences illustrated with regard to dry, wet and condensate gases show the three types of possible behavior. They are important in understanding proper recovery techniques, but they do not indicate that there are specifically different kinds of reservoir gases. Since it is impossible to tell (from the character of the condensed liquids alone or from the liquid yield of the gas) whether the gas will or will not condense to an appreciable degree within the reservoir during production, suitable experimental investigations must be made to determine phase behavior of the reservoir material.

Condensation of Water

Often overlooked are the facts that water is nearly always present in gas reservoirs and that the reservoir gas is nearly always substantially saturated with water vapor at the temperature and pressure at which it enters the wellbore. Temperature and pressure changes from subsurface to surface conditions nearly always cause condensation of part of this water—both within the well during the upward travel of the gas and in surface equipment—in the same manner that liquid condenses from a retrograde gas when temperature and pressure are dropped. To appreciate this fact, consider an example reservoir with a pressure of 4,000 pounds per square inch and temperature of 200° Fahrenheit. Gas in this reservoir is saturated with water vapor that amounts to about .7 barrel of water per million cubic feet of gas. If a well produced 5 million cubic feet of gas per day, the produced gas would contain about 3.5 barrels of water in vapor form under reservoir conditions. If this well has a tubing pressure of 2,500 pounds per square inch and a wellhead temperature of 150° Fahrenheit, 5 million cubic feet of water-saturated gas would contain only about 1.7 barrels of water in vapor form as it passes the wellhead. Pressure and temperature conditions have simply changed from the bottom to the top of the wellbore so that the gas can no longer hold as much water. In this case, 1.8 barrels of water, or about 50 per cent of the water existing in the reservoir gas, will be condensing to liquid in the wellbore every day. Much of this condensed water is carried in the flow lines into the separator as entrained droplets of water.

Free water entrained in gas becomes quite a field problem because it tends to freeze in the field equipment in the form of hydrates, rendering meters and valves inoperative. Low temperature separators solve this problem by removing the entrained water close to the wellhead before the gas arrives at trouble points. In many cases, appreciable amounts of water will settle to the bottom of the well and can, in time, saturate the producing sand surrounding the wellbore so that permeability to the flow of gas may be materially reduced. This reduction could result either from water blocking or clay swelling and could be responsible for gradual decrease in deliverability requiring periodic remedial work.

Gas Reservoir Drives

The physical environment within which gas is found influences the recovery potential of that gas. Particularly important are the texture and character of the porous rock comprising the reservoir, the variation of rock properties throughout the reservoir and the temperature and pressure.

Gas reservoirs as well as oil reservoirs can have some degree of water drive. Development, workover, producing operations and recovery are all affected by such a drive. Some gas reservoirs may have sufficient water drive to maintain or substantially maintain reservoir pressure at desired producing rates. In these cases, no appreciable retrograde condensation of the heavier hydrocarbon components would occur in the reservoir. Most condensation would occur in the wellbore or in surface separation equipment and be recovered. Little decline in condensate yield would then be observed during producing operations. Water drive gas reservoirs are generally recognized by geologic information gained during drilling operations, by pressure trends or by increasing water production during the producing life of the reservoir.

It must not be assumed that, because water drive tends to maintain pressure and minimize retrograde condensation, no problem exists in producing such a reservoir. Probably a greater problem exists because gas recovery by water drive displacement is often much less than expansion recovery by pressure blowdown and depletion.

Operating Programs

Reservoir pressure declines along with production from reservoirs that do not possess a water drive and in many that have only a limited water drive. Little or no formation water is produced from this type gas reservoir. As reservoir pressure declines with production, hydrocarbons are condensed to liquid in the reservoir, and these liquids essentially are unrecoverable. Declining condensate yields during the producing life of the reservoir is evidence of the loss; laboratory examination of reservoir gases can predict this loss before it occurs. Although recovery of gas from a reservoir is very simple and a high recovery efficiency (on the order of 85 per cent) is almost always possible, this simplicity and high efficiency does not necessarily carry over to condensate recovery.

Loss of liquid hydrocarbons in the reservoir can in some

cases be avoided economically by cycling operations. In such an operation, retrograde gas in a reservoir is produced, stripped of its condensate in suitable surface equipment, and the stripped dry gas compressed and returned to the producing formation to maintain pressure and prevent condensation in the reservoir. The retrograde gas in the formation is displaced toward the producing wells by the injected dry gas. Ultimate condensate recovery obtainable depends on the completeness with which the entire reservoir can be flushed with dry gas when the cycling project reaches its economic limit. Figs. 144 and 145 illlustrate cycling vs straight production of a gas reservoir with and without water drive.

The operator is thus confronted with three general courses by which retrograde gas reservoirs can be produced:

1. Recover condensate that leaves the reservoir in the vapor phase with the produced gas by a simple expansion process, and abandon that which condenses as retrograde liquid within the reservoir.

2. Recover the gas and its vapor-phase condensate with reservoir pressure maintained, or substantially maintained, by water drive (if such a drive is present).

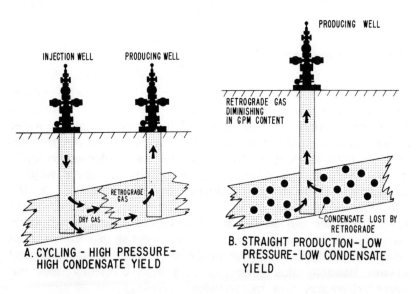

Fig. 144—*Cycling vs straight production—no water drive.*

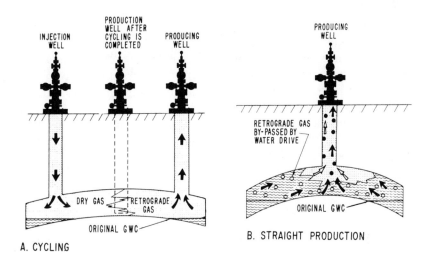

Fig. 145—*Cycling vs straight production—water drive.*

3. Cycle the reservoir for condensate recovery by re-injecting dry processed gas prior to final withdrawal of the gas reserve for sale or other disposition.

Wet Gas

A wet gas is predominantly methane but contains some intermediate hydrocarbons. No more than traces of very heavy hydrocarbons are present. Wet gas is one from which little liquid will be condensed in the reservoir as pressure declines because the temperature is high enough to keep most of the components in the gas phase. Some condensate will be formed at surface temperature, but for this category of gas the amount will be small. It is common practice, therefore, to separate butanes and heavier materials from the produced gas, either by low temperature stabilization techniques or in a gasoline plant when the amount of gas and its yield justify cost of recovery.

Dry Gas

A dry gas is composed principally of methane with only minor amounts of ethane, propane and butane. It contains very little heavy hydrocarbons. No liquid will condense from this gas, either in the reservoir or at surface temperature conditions during production. Any recovery of liquid from this type gas would require an absorption process of recovery such as used in present-day natural gasoline plants; however, this usually would not be economical.

♦

♦

♦

_____

Miscible Drive

It has long been recognized that all naturally occurring reservoir mechanisms fall far short in their ability to produce the oil contained within the reservoirs. Dissolved gas drive reservoirs, gas cap drive reservoirs, water drive reservoirs and even the most efficient combinations of these mechanisms cannot recover all the oil contained in the reservoir.

Many reasons have been offered to explain the failure to achieve complete or even 50 per cent oil recovery by natural means from virtually any oil reservoir ever discovered. These reasons include all of the problems enumerated in the foregoing chapters. They may be considered as development problems, reservoir problems, well problems, rate problems, fluid problems or any of many other specific types of problems. All are concerned with the recovery of additional quantities of the oil contained in the reservoir which otherwise is either unrecoverable or uneconomical to recover.

Much effort has been directed toward the definition and explanation of the various physical phenomena which comprise a producing oil reservoir and much has been learned of these processes. Indeed, the nature of oil itself is, paradoxically, responsible not only for its occurrence in a reservoir but also for our inability to recover all of it from a reservoir. This nature, among other things, prevents it from mixing with water, reservoir material and many other substances.

This property of definite composition with distinct boundary conditions is possessed by all tangible substances. A stone has form or shape. It remains in the same shape through the action of the forces within its molecules. It is not affected by forces outside its own molecules under usually prevailing circumstances. A stone may be subjected, however, to unusual circumstances which may overpower the molecular forces. It may be crushed into very small individual grains by the application of great pressure. It may be melted by the application of intense heat. It may be transformed into another substance entirely by the introduction of other molecules which have specific affinities for the rock molecules and cause a chemical change. These boundary conditions are controlled by forces of surface tension. Generally, solids have very high surface tension, while liquids have intermediate surface tension and gases, relatively low surface tension.

When two different substances are placed together, an interaction of the individual surface tensions occurs. This is termed interfacial tension and relates the affinity or non-affinity of the one to the other. These are the forces most important in limiting oil recovery.

The interfaces between gas and oil and between water and oil prevent gas or water from displacing completely the oil from a porous reservoir rock. This is explained in detail in Chapter 7 and illustrated in Figs. 98 through 104. If the interfacial tensions were reduced to zero, residual oil would not occur as is shown in Fig. 101 after gas displacement action—nor would it occur as is shown in Fig. 104 after water displacement action. If sufficient reduction of interfacial tension could be achieved, droplets of oil would be elongated easily and be displaced along the pore channel with the water movement (Fig. 146).

Because of this principle, considerable research has been expended over a number of years in an effort to learn how to effect a reduction of interfacial forces between oil and water in reservoir rock by means of surface active agents and detergents. Fig. 147 illustrates the concept involved if interfacial forces could be reduced to zero, thus preventing capillary forces from causing residual oil to be retained in the pore channels through which water flows. Although some success has been attained, practical field methods have yet to be devised where surface active agents or detergents can be utilized to effect total oil recovery by water displacement.

Recognizing that attaining 100 per cent oil recovery will involve some process which eliminates interfacial forces, research organizations have studied miscible drive utilizing various types and combinations of solvents or enriched gases to drive oil from reservoir rocks.

In 1949 a form of miscible displacement, now referred to as high-pressure gas injection, was launched by The Atlantic Refining Co. in Block 31, Devonian field in Crane County, Tex. Later a second form of miscible drive, now known as condensing gas drive, was developed by Humble Oil & Refining Co. and installed

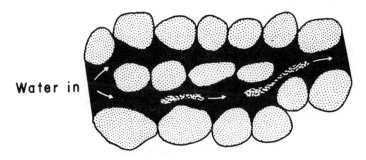

Water in

Fig. 146—*Reduced surface tension in the interfacial film moves oil through restrictions and into producing stream. (Courtesy* JOURNAL OF PETROLEUM TECHNOLOGY—*June, 1958.)*

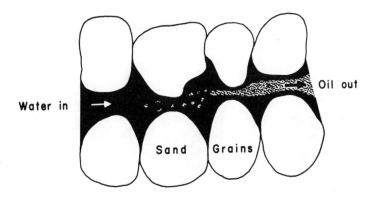

Water in

Oil out

Sand Grains

Fig. 147—*Total oil recovery achieved from pore channel where interfacial force between fluids is reduced to zero. (Courtesy* JOURNAL OF PETROLEUM TECHNOLOGY—*June, 1958.)*

in the Bronte field of Coke County, Tex., and in the Seeligson field in South Texas. About the same time, a third process of miscible displacement was developed which is now referred to as the miscible slug process. The Carter Oil Co. initiated the first successful miscible slug project in 1953 in the Seminole field, Okla. Phenominal laboratory results and some early field successes brought initiation of a large number of projects in the few years that followed.

Theory of Miscibility

Miscibility can be explained as that physical condition between two fluids that will permit them to mix in all proportions without an interface being formed between the two fluids.

Methane is shown to be a gas and oil is shown to be a liquid at atmospheric conditions of temperature and pressure (Fig. 148). In this example, methane remains a gas and oil remains a liquid under conditions of 2,000 pounds per square inch and 150° Fahrenheit. When these two materials are mixed under the ele-

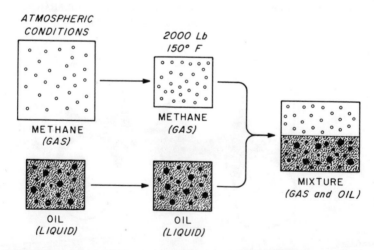

Fig. 148.—*Immiscibility of methane gas and oil liquid at reservoir conditions of temperature and pressure. (Courtesy* JOURNAL OF PETROLEUM TECHNOLOGY—*June, 1958.)*

vated conditions of temperature and pressure, the mixture remains part liquid and part gas with an interface between the two materials. Some gas goes into solution in the oil at the higher pressure and temperature; however, the two materials are considered immiscible because they do not mix in all proportions at those conditions.

Both methane and propane are shown in Fig. 149 to be gases at atmospheric conditions of temperature and pressure. Upon raising pressure, propane changes into a liquid. The methane gas and propane liquid mix in all proportions at 2,000 pounds per square inch and 150° Fahrenheit. The two materials are therefore miscible in each other at the elevated conditions of temperature and pressure. Although propane is actually a liquid, it is a gas at these conditions in the presence of gas.

Propane is shown to be a gas and oil a liquid at atmospheric conditions of temperature and pressure (Fig. 150). Propane liquid and oil liquid mix in all proportions at 2,000 pounds per square inch and 150° Fahrenheit. In this case, propane is considered a liquid in the presence of the liquid oil and propane and oil are miscible at the existing conditions.

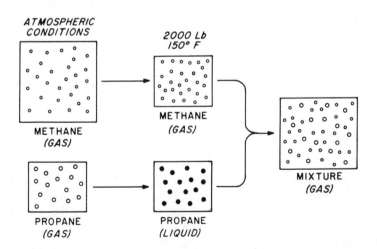

Fig. 149—*Miscibility of methane gas and propane (or LPG) liquid at reservoir conditions of temperature and pressure. Here, propane (or LPG) is a gas in the presence of gas. (Courtesy* JOURNAL OF PETROLEUM TECHNOLOGY—*June, 1958.)*

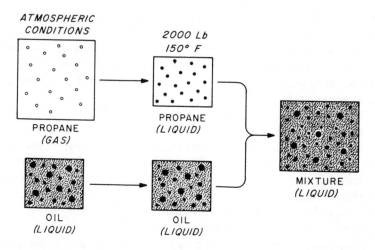

Fig. 150—*Miscibility of propane (or LPG) liquid and oil at reservoir conditions of temperature and pressure. Here, propane (or LPG) liquid is a liquid in the presence of a liquid. (Courtesy* JOURNAL OF PETROLEUM TECHNOLOGY—*June, 1958.)*

The physical state in which propane occurs depends upon the state of the materials in whose presence it occurs and the conditions of temperature and pressure under which they occur. It can occur as either gas or liquid at increased pressure. It is this characteristic of propane, LPG and certain solvents which provides the basis upon which the miscible drive process works.

How Miscible Drive Works

Oil in a reservoir can be displaced from the rock with a high degree of efficiency by a solvent which is miscible with the oil. This occurs because there is no interface between the two materials and therefore no capillary forces to retain the oil in the pore channels through which the solvent flows. This has been known for many years and solvents have been used to clean cores of their residual oil for core analysis measurements. Oil-miscible solvents, however, are expensive and for many years miscible displacement, although efficient, seemed uneconomic because of the cost of the great quantity of materials thought necessary to replace all of the oil produced.

The present-day miscible drive methods utilize the oil-miscibility principle; however, the methods are engineered to accomplish all the good features of miscible displacement while leaving relatively inexpensive gas in the reservoir space vacated by displaced oil. The process is accomplished by utilizing a minimum amount of solvent (propane, LPG or other solvent) as a buffer or scavenger ahead of injected gas. Solvent must stay between the oil and gas at all times to maintain the miscible drive process (Fig. 151). Where this takes place, the miscible drive process can be expected to provide total recovery of the oil from the individual pore channels.

Solvent may be used to displace residual oil left behind a conventional gas drive (Fig. 101). This displacement process is accomplished by the solvent's enclosing and mixing with the oil. This eliminates the interfaces that existed between the oil and gas and permits the oil to flow out of the pore channel where it had been trapped under the conventional gas drive process (Fig. 152).

Solvent also may be used to displace residual oil left behind a conventional water drive (Fig. 153). This displacement process is accomplished by the solvent's flowing through the large pore channels, contacting the residual oil, building up a bank of oil ahead, and displacing it on toward the well. In this case a bank

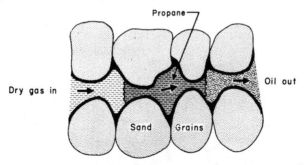

Fig. 151—*Miscible drive, with propane as a solvent between oil and gas. Interfacial forces are reduced to zero and total oil recovery from the pore channel is obtained. (Courtesy* JOURNAL OF PETROLEUM TECHNOLOGY—*June, 1958.)*

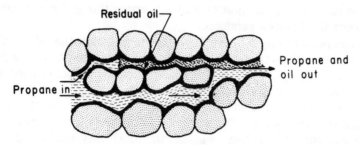

Fig. 152—*Propane solvent contacts residual oil in tight pore channel left by gas drive, thus breaking the interface and allowing the oil to flow out of the tight pore channel. (Courtesy* JOURNAL OF PETROLEUM TECHNOLOGY—*June, 1958.)*

of water will be built up ahead of the solvent which in turn is ahead of the gas used to drive the solvent.

Types of Miscible Drive

There are several approaches toward achieving miscible drive in a reservoir. Gas cycling actually falls under the classification of miscible drive operations since the injected gas is completely miscible with the reservoir gas. Recovery in these operations is not hampered by fluid capillary forces, however, and is essentially

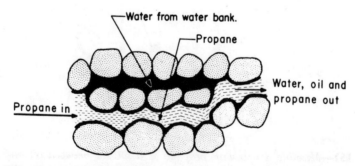

Fig. 153—*Propane solvent moves into high permeability pore channel, mixes with residual oil left by water drive and causes oil to flow out. (Courtesy* JOURNAL OF PETROLEUM TECHNOLOGY—*June, 1958.)*

complete in those pore spaces through which injected gas passes. Recovery of condensate gas from low permeability and dead-end pore channels is not obtained during gas cycling operations. After cycling, however, a part of the rich gas may be recovered from such areas of the reservoir during blowdown operations by gas expansion or by water drive.

In miscible displacement of oil there are three general types of drive processes. They differ in the manner in which the solvent bank is created between the oil and the displacing gas. These processes are (1) miscible slug process, (2) condensing gas drive and (3) high pressure gas drive.

Miscible Slug Process

The miscible slug process consists of injecting a quantity of solvent into an oil reservoir and pushing this liquid bank toward producing wells with gas injected behind the solvent. Injected solvent being miscible with reservoir oil results in efficient displacement of the oil (Fig. 151). This is analogous to cleaning cores in the laboratory with solvents.

Gas Drive Processes

Though not thermodynamically rigorous, the qualitative triangular phase diagram best illustrates the gas drive processes. In Fig. 154 the complex hydrocarbon system is arbitrarily shown in three groups of components analogous to a three-component system. Any point within the triangular graph represents a hydrocarbon mixture with specific amounts of each of the three groups of components: methane (C_1), ethane (C_2) through hexane (C_6), and heptane and heavier components (C_{7+}). Conditions for a given graph are at some constant temperature and pressure.

An area of the graph is surrounded by a loop called the phase boundary curve within which the mixture exists in two phases — gas and liquid. "Tie lines" are cut across the two-phase region. These tie lines terminate at points on a saturated vapor curve and a saturated liquid curve, respectively. These two points represent a saturated gas and a saturated oil that would be in

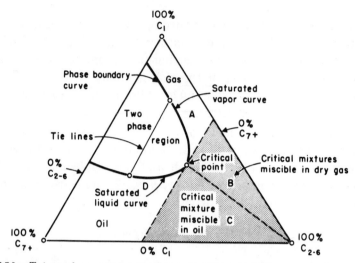

Fig. 154—*Triangular graph showing physical conditions of hydrocarbon systems of fixed temperature and pressure conditions. (Courtesy* JOURNAL OF PETROLEUM TECHNOLOGY—*June, 1958.)*

equilibrium with each other if placed in contact at the temperature and pressure existing for the given diagram.

The limiting tie line is a point representing the critical mixture for the existing temperature and pressure. Mixtures represented by points above and to the right of the saturated vapor curve are gas (Area A), and mixtures represented by points below and to the left of the saturated liquid curve are oil (Area D).

Mixtures with greater percentages of intermediate components, or those lying to the right and down, are in the zone that is either liquid or gas if they can be visibly defined in the presence of one or the other. This is the area of critical mixtures. A portion of this critical area lies upward and to the right of the two-phase area (Area B), and contain compositions composed of less heptane plus (C_{7+}) components which are miscible in mixtures represented by points in the gas area. The other portion of the critical area of mixtures lies down and to the right of the two-phase area (Area C). Mixtures in this area have less methane (C_1) component and are miscible in mixtures represented by points in the oil area.

The molecular behavior of hydrocarbon mixtures is governed

by the four important physical factors: (1) pressure, (2) kinetic energy associated with temperature, (3) molecular attraction and (4) molecular repulsion. (See Chapter 3.) Oil and gas, either together or separate in a reservoir, may undergo drastic physical changes in state as they move from point to point in a reservoir because of these fundamental governing features of molecular behavior. These basic fundamentals therefore explain the phase behavior of reservoir oil and gas in the process of recovery of reservoir oil by gas displacement.

Equilibrium Gas Drive: An equilibrium gas drive, such as straight gas cap drive, is the process of oil displacement by gas in which little or no mass component exchange occurs between either the oil mixture being displaced or the gas mixture displacing the oil. Fig. 155 illustrates this type of displacement by a triangular diagram showing the hydrocarbon aspects and a schematic block diagram showing the recovery characteristics of displacement. Gas A and Oil A are located at the terminal points of a tie line across the two-phase area on the saturated vapor curve and saturated oil curve, respectively. The schematic saturation-distance diagram shows that partial oil displacement occurs with this type of drive; however, because the gas and oil are immiscible, capillary characteristics of the rock are controlling features. The capillary forces cause the rock to be highly retentive to the remaining oil with only relatively small percentages of oil pushed ahead and recovered by the gas as it moves through the rock.

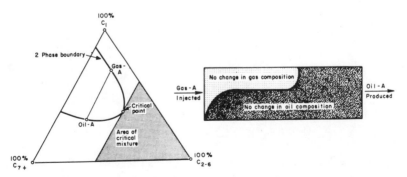

Fig. 155—*Equilibrium gas drive — triangular graph showing no change in composition of displacing gas and displaced oil. (Courtesy* PETROLEUM ENGINEER—*Sept., 1955.)*

Condensing Gas Drive: In the condensing gas drive process a gas which is rich in intermediate hydrocarbon components, such as propane, is injected into the reservoir. A transition bank is subsequently formed between the oil in the reservoir and the injected gas. This occurs because oil absorbs the propane from the gas through attractive forces between the oil and propane materials. It functions in the same manner as an absorber oil removing LPG from gas through molecular attraction in a gasoline plant operation.

The stepwise process of gas displacing oil by this method starts with contact of injected Gas B with Oil B (Fig. 156). A mass exchange of components between these two materials results in the loss of some intermediates by Gas B, changing its composition to Gas 1 in equilibrium with Oil 1. This has resulted from absorption of intermediate components by Oil B.

After Gas B contacts oil in several consecutive steps, the oil changes by absorption of more intermediates from Oil B to Oil 1, to Oil 2, to Oil 3 and then to oil at the critical point or a critical mixture. When this occurs, the two phases flash into one across the interface. The composition change in the reservoir is from displacing Gas B to a critical mixture, Oil 3, Oil 2, Oil 1 and displaced Oil B without a change in phase being present. This transition is shown schematically as a bank in the block diagram in Fig. 156.

For this process to occur where ordinary black oil is involved

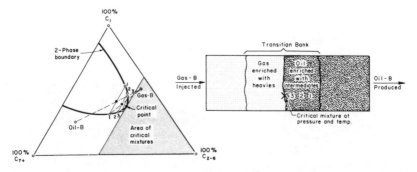

Fig. 156—*Condensing gas drive, critical displacement—oil is displaced from sand by gas components which condense to form a critical mixture and transition bank at the front. (Courtesy* Petroleum Engineer—*Sept., 1955.)*

(with composition represented by points in Area D of Fig. 154), the composition of the displacing gas must occur in the critical mixture region, Area B. Should the composition of the gas be less rich in intermediate components and occur in Area A of Fig. 154, a condensing gas drive may still occur; however, the process would not continue to complete miscibility. This limited process would be termed a "non-critical condensing gas drive" process, whereas the process that continues to miscibility would be termed a "critical condensing gas drive" process. More recovery is usually experienced from a non-critical process than from equilibrium gas drive; however, maximum recovery is attained under miscible conditions.

High Pressure Gas Drive: A miscible drive can be created using gas having percentages of intermediates lower than that of a critical gas mixture (Area A of Fig. 154). The oil involved, however, must be rich in intermediates and occur in Area C of Fig. 154.

The stepwise process of gas displacing oil by this method

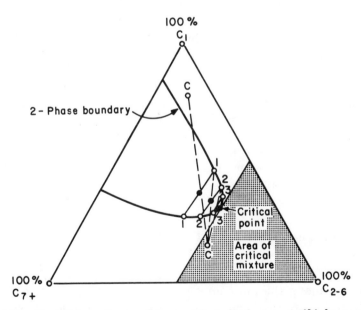

Fig. 157—*Vaporizing-oil, gas drive, critical displacement (high pressure gas drive process)—oil is displaced by oil components which vaporize to form a critical mixture and transition bank at the front.*

occurs first with contact of injected Gas C with Oil C (Fig. 157). A mass exchange of components between these two materials results in Gas C's gaining some intermediates and changing composition to Gas 1 in equilibrium with Oil 1. This has resulted from the loss by vaporization of some of the intermediate components of Oil C.

After Gas C contacts oil in several consecutive steps, the gas changes by vaporization of more oil intermediates from Gas C to Gas 1, to Gas 2, to Gas 3, to gas at the critical point or a critical mixture. When this occurs, the two phases flash into one across the interface. The composition change in the reservoir is from displacing Gas C to Gas 1, Gas 2, Gas 3, a critical mixture, and displaced Oil C without a change in phase being present. This transition is shown schematically the same as in that of Fig. 156.

For this process to occur the composition of the oil must have high content of intermediate components and occur in the Area C of Fig. 154 for the existing conditions of temperature and pressure. Should the composition of the oil be less rich in intermediate components and occur in Area D of Fig. 154, vaporization of some oil may still occur; however, the process would not continue to complete miscibility. This limited process may be considered a "non-critical vaporizing-oil gas drive" process, whereas the process that continues to miscibility may be considered a "critical vaporizing-oil gas drive" process. Because this process usually occurs only under high pressure conditions, it is commonly referred to as the "high pressure gas drive process".

This process, like condensing gas drive, provides additional recovery under non-critical conditions compared to equilibrium displacement; however, maximum recovery is attained under miscible conditions.

Factors Influencing Miscible Drive Processes

There are a number of factors influencing miscible drive processes. Among the most important of these factors are composition of the injected gas, composition of the displaced oil, temperature and pressure.

In the condensing gas drive process the composition of the gas is more important than composition of the displaced oil. The composition of the oil is somewhat important but in an indirect way. So long as the injected gas is a critical mixture, most oils will become miscible with the gas (Fig. 158). Heavy oils will require more contact with the rich gas and, therefore, a greater length of fluid transition zone will occur. With light oils, however, the process occurs faster and the transition zone is shorter.

In the vaporizing-oil gas drive process the composition of the oil and the existing pressure are more important than composition of the injected gas (Fig. 159). Dry gases will require greater contact with the oil than will rich gas; however, this presents little problem because of the rapidity of mass component exchange.

Conditions of reservoir pressure and temperature at which a project can be operated controls whether or not miscibility can be attained and which miscible drive process can best be applied. Pressure is particularly important because the area of critical mixtures on the triangular phase diagram becomes larger (i.e., the area of two-phase occurrence becomes smaller) with increased pressure, allowing both heavier oils and leaner gases to be critical mixtures (Fig. 160).

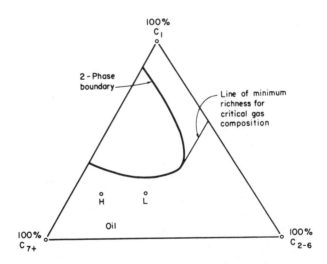

Fig. 158—*Criteria for determining composition of a critical gas for a given reservoir pressure and temperature. (Courtesy* PETROLEUM ENGINEER—*Sept., 1955.)*

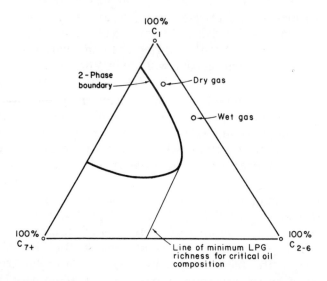

Fig. 159—*Criteria for determining composition of a critical oil for a given reservoir pressure and temperature.*

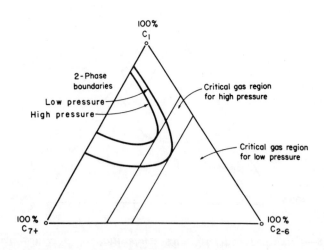

Fig. 160—*Effects of pressure on the composition of critical mixtures. (Courtesy* PETROLEUM ENGINEER—*Sept., 1955.)*

Factors Influencing Application of
Miscible Drive to Reservoirs

There are a large number of factors that influence applicability of miscible drive to reservoirs. Among the most important of these factors are reservoir size and shape, irregularity of porosity and permeability of the reservoir rock, structural dip of the reservoir, nature of reservoir oil and gas in place, conditions of reservoir pressure and temperature and existing fluid saturations in the reservoir.

Reservoir Size and Shape

Since a miscible drive process involves injection operations and since recovery from the reservoir depends upon reservoir coverage of the displacing fluids, it is necessary that injected fluids contact a maximum number of pore spaces throughout the area of the reservoir. This is complicated by the fact that fluids are injected at single points in the reservoir. The areal coverage or pattern efficiency of the project is controlled by the geometric nature of the reservoir and the points of entry of the displacing fluids into the reservoir. Within a given reservoir the pattern or area of the reservoir affected by displacing material is considerably smaller than the total area of the reservoir (Fig. 107). While the geometric shape of the reservoir cannot be altered, the pattern efficiency of the displacing fluids can be controlled to some degree by the location, rate and timing of fluid production and injection or the manner in which the normal drive is controlled. The various geometric patterns of water injection in the case of water floods such as 5-spot, 9-spot, line drive, etc., are recognized and well known; however, pattern considerations are applicable to all reservoir oil displacement operations, including reservoirs under primary producing conditions. These various operations must be studied and the best pattern utilized if maximum reservoir coverage by the project is to be obtained.

The great mobility of gas compared to the more viscous oil presents a very important problem because pattern efficiency will be small in the case of miscible drive in reservoirs having little structural dip. Use of water as an injected fluid behind a gas-driven miscible drive project may improve the pattern under applicable conditions. Proper design of such a project provides for features to prevent water from overrunning the gas and bank of solvent materials ahead (Fig. 161).

Irregularity of Porosity and Permeability

Variations in porosity and permeability of reservoir rock are among the most important reservoir factors that control displacement of oil by miscible drive. Reservoir rock porosity and permeability always vary to some degree from one pore channel to the next. In addition, reservoir rock almost universally is formed in layers, or stratified, either to a small extent or over larger distances. The layering can be merely differences in porosity and permeability of layers in capillary equilibrium, or the layering can be separated by impermeable shale or other rock streaks.

Fluids of different density and viscosity flowing through a single pore channel have a tendency to overrun each other and mix, and the tendency is increased in the case where a dense fluid such as oil is pushed by a light fluid such as gas in the miscible drive process. This condition is multiplied many fold by the irregularity encountered between the great number of pore channels present in even the most regular sand and is a natural condition with which to reckon. Displacement efficiency, therefore, may be reduced because of solvent and dry gas production through this

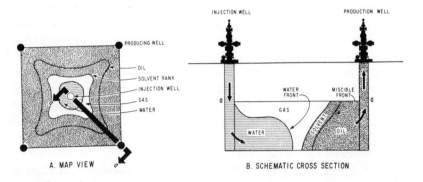

Fig. 161—*Miscible drive in a 5-spot, with water following gas and solvent to improve pattern efficiency.*

intermixing before the expected ultimate oil recovery is obtained.

The nature of layering or zoning of the reservoir rock, one of the most important factors involved in reservoir irregularity, must be determined by geological studies so that a project can be designed for maximum pattern efficiency.

The irregularity of the reservoir determines the conformance efficiency of the recovery process. (See Chapter 7.) A reservoir having a high conformance efficiency is shown in Fig. 162. Because total oil recovery is obtained by miscible drive in the conformance area, which here is a large part of the reservoir volume, the over-all reservoir oil recovery is extremely high. A reservoir having low conformance efficiency to miscible drive is shown in Fig. 163. Here, over-all recovery obtainable is intermediate in magnitude because of the small volume of rock conforming to the displacing action from which total recovery may be obtained by the project.

Where the conformance efficiency is low for miscible drive, it may be sufficiently high under water drive so that in some cases over-all oil recovery may be higher for water drive than

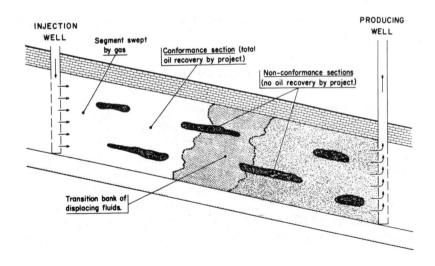

Fig. 162—*Reservoir having high conformance efficiency, with consequent high over-all recovery efficiency. (Courtesy* PETROLEUM ENGINEER—*Sept., 1957.)*

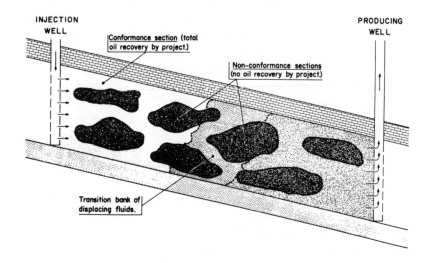

INJECTION
WELL

Conformance section (total
oil recovery by project.)

Non-conformance sections
(no oil recovery by project.)

PRODUCING
WELL

Transition bank of
displacing fluids.

Fig. 163—*Reservoir having low conformance efficiency, with consequent intermediate over-all recovery efficiency. (Courtesy* PETROLEUM ENGINEER—*Sept., 1957.)*

for miscible drive. For best project design, therefore, these factors must be properly recognized.

Structural Dip

Because the miscible drive process is one in which gas is the energy source for oil displacement, gravity segregation is of great importance in providing maximum utilization of energy from the gas source. Steeply dipping reservoirs permit oil to segregate ahead of gas, resulting in a more clearly defined transition bank of solvent separating the oil and gas phases. The reservoir thickness, its irregularity, and the degree to which it is stratified all have their geometrical influence, however, upon the ability of gravity to influence the displacement process in the best manner.

Nature of the Reservoir

The composition of reservoir oil has a definite influence upon the degree to which miscible drive is applicable to the reservoir. Generally speaking, an oil having high shrinkage characteristics because of high content of intermediate hydrocarbon components will be more suitable for a miscible drive operation. Less over-all amounts of solvent will be needed in the injected gas, or as a slug, because of the presence of such solvent materials already in the reservoir oil. Heavy oils will cause more by-passing by the solvent and gas because of high mobility and, therefore, will require considerably greater over-all quantities of solvent in the process.

Conditions of Reservoir Temperature and Pressure

Reservoir pressure and oil and gas compositions are interrelated and one or more must be controlled or adjusted if a miscible drive project is to perform properly. For a given oil at a given reservoir temperature, either pressure must be controlled or composition of injected gas must be controlled for miscibility to be attained. If the oil is a light, high shrinkage oil and the pressure of displacement can be maintained sufficiently high for the given oil, the vaporizing-oil gas drive process may be attained utilizing dry gas. If reservoir pressure cannot be maintained sufficiently high for the given oil to be a critical mixture, then either the condensing gas drive process utilizing rich gas or the miscible slug process will be required.

Fluid Saturation in Reservoir Rocks

Some reservoir materials are nearly always produced before a miscible drive project is considered by an operator for the reservoir. The original capillary equilibrium of the reservoir fluids is thereby nearly always upset and a gas saturation will be present in the rock pore spaces. There is a tendency, therefore, for solvents or condensing gas to move through the gas-saturated pore channels—thus by-passing the oil saturation in these channels prior to the formation of a miscible bank of fluids. In laboratory experiments this effect has not been found to be of any appreciable magnitude; however, in the reservoir itself experience has indicated the problem of by-passing and deterioration of the miscible zone is of much greater magnitude.

Miscible Project Design Considerations

The over-all design of a miscible drive project will vary from reservoir to reservoir. Like other methods of increasing oil recovery by fluid injection, the process will probably require installation of special surface equipment such as storage, pipelines and handling facilities. These facilities are likely to require special design depending upon circumstances. For example, in the case of vaporizing-oil gas drive projects (high pressure gas injection-type projects), the required equipment would be similar to normal gas injection projects with respect to surface lines and compressor facilities, but would require special design to suit the pressure demands (Fig. 164). On the other hand, injection of propane, LPG or enriched gas in low pressure projects would require special storage and pumping equipment to handle the materials (Fig. 165). In the case of condensing gas drive, special pumping and metering equipment would be necessary to assure that ethane,

Fig. 164—*Atlantic Refining Co.'s high pressure gas injection miscible drive project — Block 31, Devonian field, Crane County, Tex., showing injection well (foreground) and gas plant (background).*
(Courtesy Atlantic Refining Co.)

Fig. 165—*Atlantic's miscible slug project showing temporary propane injection pumps (foreground) and separator (background)— Slaughter field, Cochran, Terry, and Hockley Counties, Tex. (Courtesy Atlantic Refining Co.)*

propane, butane or LPG is accurately blended with gas to create the desired composition for injection (Fig. 166).

Certainly in any project that involves injection of solvents or enriched gas, separation equipment must be adequate to assure recovery of substantial portions of these components from the produced materials later in the project. Economics would, of course, dictate whether this would involve standard lease separation, low temperature separation or gasoline plant facilities.

The composition and volume of injected fluids for a particular miscible drive application will be governed by reservoir characteristics and availability of products. In general, it may be assumed that the greater the percentage of methane that can be used in the injection fluid to effect miscible displacement, the lower will be the cost of the total material injection. The cost of the material, however, will usually be influenced by the market demand in the vicinity and the transportation cost necessary to deliver the materials to the point of application. In this regard, the price of materials is not usually prohibitive, but in many cases the transportation distance may be great. Volume requirements for propane or LPG may be such that installation of a pipeline cannot be justified and supply must depend on trucking and adequate storage.

Since availability of propane and LPG is seasonal in many areas, their use in slug-type operations during an off-market

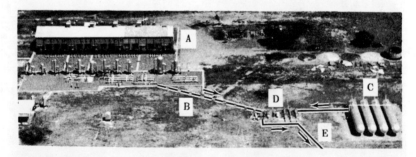

Fig. 166—*Humble Oil & Refining Co.'s condensing gas drive project, Seeligson field, Zone 20-B, Jim Wells and Kleberg Counties, Tex., showing gas compressor station (A), dry gas injection line (B), propane supply tanks (C), propane injection pumps (D), and enriched gas injection line (E). (Courtesy Humble Oil & Refining Co.)*

demand period may greatly enhance economics of the over-all project. Rate of production may be tied in with availability of injected materials, since reservoir pressure must not be allowed to drop below some given point for the conditions involved. In other cases, dry gas is often available in areas where demand for it is not pressing; in such areas its use can be inexpensive and very beneficial in recovering additional oil using either of the processes.

As is the case in almost any secondary recovery or pressure maintenance operation, it normally is desirable to conduct a pilot-type project on a portion of the reservoir to evaluate more fully miscible drive requirements and recovery potential. A pilot operation is usually more involved for a miscible drive process than for the usual waterflood or gas drive operation and normally requires more investment in surface facilities. For this reason, the pilot project is designed so that it can be readily expanded, if desired, to a full scale operation.

Potential increase in ultimate oil recovery is, of course, a most attractive feature associated with miscible drive operations; however, this is not the only desirable factor. As is often the case in other types of pressure maintenance operations, it is possible to produce a reservoir over longer periods of time with highly maintained rates of production. Current income benefits may be obtainable through higher production rates. Also, the injection of propane, LPG or enriched gas may be performed as a temporary products storage program depending on market situations. Miscible drive operations, therefore, provide an operator with many alternatives for oil production and greatly enlarge his opportunities for increasing reserves and profits from reservoirs.

◆

◆

◆

C H A P T E R   14

Thermal Oil Recovery

P. D. WHITE | *TEJAS PETROLEUM ENGINEERS*
JON T. MOSS | *DALLAS, TEXAS*

The possibility of using heat to increase oil recovery from depleted fields has been considered seriously for nearly half a century, beginning with work by the U. S. Bureau of Mines. Numerous attempts have been made to apply heat to oil-bearing formations through the injection of hot gases, steam or hot water, and the use of electrical heaters. Heat applications to remedy wellbore problems, such as wax removal or viscosity reduction, have been widespread in the industry for numerous years. Heat as a recovery mechanism has developed slowly due to the costs involved in terms of both process equipment and technological development, but thermal oil recovery has gained momentum during the past 10 years; several steam injection and in-situ combustion projects are now operating and thermal stimulation has been applied to several hundred wells on a cyclic basis.

The in-situ combustion process of oil recovery supplies energy to move crude oil into producing wellbores by injecting air into the reservoir to support combustion of in-place crude oil. A small portion of in-place oil is burned, furnishing heat to the reservoir and its fluids. By generating the heat within the oil-bearing rock, losses are minimized and maximum utilization of the heat generated is effected. Here again, the concept is not new. United States patents were issued in 1923, and the first field experiments with the process were conducted in the Soviet Union in the late 1930's. Since 1948, significant progress has been made through laboratory investigations and numerous field tests of the process, starting with pilot work conducted independently by Mobil and Sinclair in 1952.

Field tests using steam injection occurred as early as 1933, but little additional interest was shown until 1954 when Standard Oil Co. (N.J.) started an experimental pilot project. Shell conducted early projects in Europe, Canada and Venezuela, and started California's first project in the Yorba Linda field in 1958. Since then, the number of steam injection projects has increased rapidly. Equipment manufacturers supplied the oil industry with portable, packaged steam generators which contributed significantly to the increased use of steam injection.

Steam Drive

Steam injection increases the reservoir temperature and displaces oil as shown by Fig. 167. The temperature distribution indicates steam entering the oil-bearing formation at the saturation temperature and pressure. As the steam front moves away from the injection well, the temperature gradually decreases due to pressure drop in the formation, and it has a rather sharp temperature change at the displacement front.

The lower curve of Fig. 167 shows various displacement ⌐ones caused by steam injection. Oil has been reduced to residual saturation in Zone 1, which has been swept by steam. Ahead of Zone 1, steam is condensing in Zone 2, and the resulting hot water drive displaces oil to Zone 3, which is a cold oil bank region. These saturation distributions illustrate that both steam and hot water displace oil effectively due to the decrease in oil viscosity at elevated temperatures and the resulting improvement in oil mobility. In addition, the thermal expansion of reservoir fluids assists in displacing oil, and a large percentage of oil is displaced by steam distillation. The latter is probably the most significant advantage of steam injection as compared to hot water floods.

Residual oil saturation in the various zones can be determined from laboratory studies. Process variables, such as steam pressure and temperature, oil distillation characteristics, viscosity, gravity, etc., cause wide variations in oil residuals. Another important feature is the character of the formation matrix; therefore, laboratory tests should be conducted using formation material. Many studies of this type indicate steam zones residuals ranging from 10 to 40 per cent, with the higher residual oil associated with low API oil gravity, high oil viscosity, and silty formation materials. Calculations based on sweep and displacement efficiency in high-porosity reservoirs indicate that steam displacement should recover 30 to 45 per cent of the in-place oil at oil-to-steam ratios ranging from 0.2 or 0.4 bbl oil/bbl steam, assuming favorable conditions of temperature, pressure and oil saturation.

Steam Injection Equipment

A typical steam generator is shown in Fig. 168. The ones generally in use produce about 80 per cent quality steam and

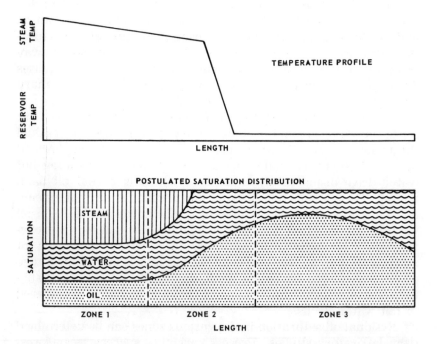

Fig. 167—*Temperature and saturation distribution during steam drive injection. (Courtesy* THE OIL AND GAS JOURNAL—*Aug. 23, 1965.)*

vary in size between 10 and 25 million Btu/hr output. Since low-quality steam is produced, relatively poor feed water can be tolerated by the single pass equipment, and all of the output is usually injected in the formation. The generator and auxiliary water-treating equipment are automated for semi-attended operation so that one operator can service several generators. Fuels can be gas or oil, and many units are operating using produced crude oil.

Fig. 169 illustrates heat losses associated with hot fluid injection. Equipment is installed so as to minimize these losses. Surface lines are insulated, and wellbore losses are reduced by injecting through tubing, which is often set on a packer. Nitrogen is frequently injected in the annulus as further means of protecting the casing from thermal stresses.

In addition to steam equipment, suitable pumping equipment and treating and storage facilities must be provided for the increased oil rates.

Thermal Stimulation by Cyclic Steam Injection

Cyclic steam injection for short periods gives quick production response by heating viscous oil formations near the wellbore. Typical cyclic programs have 20 to 40 wells serviced by each generator so that one or more wells are on injection while the others are produced.

Fig. 168—*Steam injection project, May Fee property, Kern River oil field, Kern County, Calif. From left to right are water treating equipment, steam generator and water storage. (Courtesy* CARL T. LONG, CRESTMONT OIL & GAS CO.)

Initial production response ranges from 3 to 20 times the normal oil rate before treatment. This response is attributed to viscosity reduction, wellbore clean up, and increased pressure. Treatments used in California inject from 30 to 200 bbl of water (as steam)/ft of formation treated. Produced oil ranges from 0.2 to 3.0 bbl oil/bbl steam.

Oil recovered per cycle depends on the amount of steam injected, the number of cycles, sand thickness, oil properties and primary producing characteristics. The recovery per cycle usually decreases with succeeding cycles. The time of ultimate primary recovery for a given field can be greatly accelerated by cyclic steam injection, and the total recovery can be increased by secondary programs to supplement the reservoir drive. Cyclic

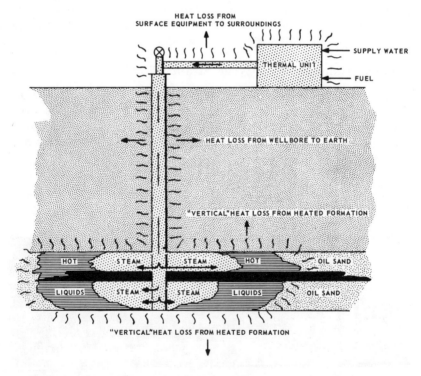

Fig. 169—*Over-all heat transmission in any hot fluid injection project may appear too complex for predicting. These losses can be broken down into parts for calculation by known methods.*
(Courtesy PETROLEUM ENGINEER—*Nov., 1964.)*

performance in thick reservoirs can be improved by diverting injection so that steam enters previously untreated sand zones.

In California many of the thick sand sections producing by gravity drainage have experienced excellent response to cyclic programs. Depleted reservoirs do not respond, but thinner sand sections can be highly productive if the reservoir pressure has duction wells. Oil in the formation is ignited when sufficient not been dissipated, although the number of cycles will probably be less. In addition, most steam operations are confined to highly viscous crude oils (generally less than 15° API) and to less than 3,000 ft depth.

Combustion Drive

The in-situ combustion process is effective in many of the same types of reservoirs where steam appears applicable, but depth is not a limiting factor because heat is generated within the reservoir. Furthermore, this process operates over a wide range of gravity and oil viscosity, depending on the burning characteristics of the particular reservoir.

How the In-Situ Combustion Process Works

The in-situ combustion process is basically a burning front that slowly moves from the air injection well to the oil production wells. The process is initiated by injecting air into a centrally located injection well surrounded by an array of pro-permeability to gas has been developed to insure adequate injectivity of air as the burning front moves radially away from the injection well. One of the industry's large air injection stations is shown in Fig. 170.

Combustion is started in the formation by injecting air at temperatures between 400 and 1,200°F, depending primarily on the low-temperature oxidization characteristics of the crude oil being ignited. Usually the injected air is pre-heated at the sand face of the injection well by an electrical heater, gas burner or some other convenient method of supplying heat. However, ignition occurs spontaneously in some reservoirs after air has been injected over some length of time. After ignition the burning front moves radially outward from the injection well at a rate governed principally by the type and amount of fuel burned and the air injection rate.

As the burning front moves away from the injection well,

several distinct zones develop and a number of different, but intimately related, mechanisms are operative. These zones are illustrated in Fig. 171, which depicts a cross section of the burning front between the injection well and one of the production wells. The upper portion of Fig. 171 illustrates the corresponding formation temperature.

Burning Front

The crude oil immediately ahead of the high-temperature burning front is carbonized to produce a coke-like deposit on the sand grains. This deposit constitutes the principal fuel for the process. Left behind the burning front is hot, clean sand which is effectively utilized to heat the injected air before it reaches the burning zone. Maximum temperatures of 600 to 1,500°F have been observed at the burning front.

Thermal Cracking

Further downstream of the burning zone, the temperature is high enough to vaporize the lighter hydrocarbons which move forward into the cooler reservoir and condense. Nearer the burning front the temperature is high enough to convert the interstitial water to steam, which also moves forward and condenses in the cooler sand. Immediately ahead of the burning front, high temperatures result in thermal cracking of the heavy hydrocarbons left on the sand. Products of this thermal cracking are petroleum coke and gaseous hydrocarbons. The hydrocarbon gases also move ahead of the front and partially condense in the cooler sand, while the petroleum coke is deposited on the sand grains and becomes fuel for the process.

Condensing Steam Drive

As the injected air reacts with the residual fuel at the burning front, steam is one of the products formed. This steam, along with that produced by vaporizing the interstitial water of the formation, moves forward and contacts the cooler sand ahead of the front. The steam loses heat rapidly to the formation and results in a condensing steam-type drive. The large amount of latent heat released by condensation of this steam imparts substantial energy to the oil in and ahead of the steam zone. This greatly decreases the viscosity of the oil and increases its mobility, which in turn enhances displacement of the oil.

Fig. 170—*In-situ combustion project, West Newport field, Orange County, Calif. From left to right are transformers, cooling tower, water storage tank, heat exchange manifold and 2,580-hp air compression installation. (Courtesy G. E. KADANE & SONS.)*

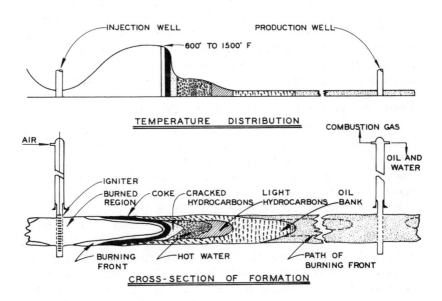

Fig. 171—*Combustion drive mechanism created by in-situ combustion of oil in the reservoir showing various distinct zones between injection and production wells.*

Distillation, Cracking and Blending

Hydrocarbon gases evolved by the normal distillation procedure mix with the hydrocarbon gases formed in the cracking reaction, and the combined streams blend and condense in the oil bank ahead. Blending of these lighter hydrocarbon gases with the oil ahead of the front, together with the heat imparted to the oil when they condense, makes the oil more mobile and improves the oil displacement.

Gas Drive

A very effective gas drive is formed. Combustion gases generated at the burning front transfer heat to the oil and further assist in reducing the viscosity of the oil by partially dissolving in it. The oil bank that forms ahead of the steam zone is displaced physically by the combustion gases.

Thermal Characteristics

These intimately connected displacement mechanisms resulting from in-situ combustion form an efficient drive. In addition, thermal energy is transferred to the formation above, below and ahead of the burning front by convection in the reservoir fluids and by conduction through the formation rock itself. No other oil recovery process has the ability to effect displacement of fluids across an impermeable zone and assist oil displacement.

Variations of the Combustion Drive Process

In the basic in-situ combustion process, the burning front is supported by the injection of compressed air. Other gaseous mixtures may be used, however. The injection of air, natural gas and recycle gases has been found feasible in field tests. In another field test, steam, exhaust combustion gases and air were injected to move the heat front through the reservoir.

Since the cost of compressing air is a major expense in the combustion process, it has been proposed that catalysts be employed which cause the burning reaction to form carbon monoxide rather than carbon dioxide. This would reduce the amount of air required for combustion. In some reservoirs where air injection rates are limited by low permeability, it might be desirable to reduce the injection requirements by oxygen enrichment if economic conditions permit. Another interesting variation to the combustion process is that of reverse combustion. In this process, after burning is initiated, the direction of air flow is reversed and the burning front moves from the production well toward the injection well in a reverse manner.

Laboratory experiments and heat-transfer calculations indicate that high oil recoveries may be obtained without breakthrough of the burning front to the production wells. Movement of the burning front over about three-quarters of the distance toward the production wells might be sufficient to achieve high oil recovery. By conduction alone, elevated temperatures would cover the remaining distance to the production well. This method of partial burnout may increase oil production from a period of several months to more than a year after combustion is stopped. The rate of oil recovery could be accelerated by injecting exhaust combustion gases, water or other fluids which would increase the rate of heat transfer to the unburned region. It is apparent, however, that all of the variations to the combustion process are quite similar and depend basically on moving a high temperature zone through the formation. One of the most significant process developments involves the simultaneous injection of water and air to form a combination thermal drive.

Combination Thermal Drive (CTD)

Fig. 172 shows an effective means of scavenging heat left stored behind the burning front so that it is utilized to heat the unburned portion of the reservoir. The temperature distribution in Fig. 172A depicts the in-situ combustion process as previously described. The burning front velocity in a linear system V_{BF} is directly related to the air injection rate. The convective cooling front velocity V_C is only about 20 per cent of V_{BF} due to the low heat capacity of injected air. The heat moved forward by convection, conduction, etc. establishes a heat front which precedes the combustion front at a velocity V_H. Temperatures in the zone usually approach saturated steam temperatures.

The CTD process is shown by Fig. 172B. Water is injected simultaneously with air. The burning front velocity V_{BF} and peak temperatures are shown to be identical to normal combustion. The added water, however, is flashed to steam so that the steam front velocity V_S approaches V_{BF}. Heat scavenged from the burned sand is transferred by air and super-heated steam to the steam condensation zone ahead of the combustion front, which increases V_H. The ratio of water to air at the burning front is regulated in the CTD process to transfer 70 to 90 per cent of the effective heat generated after heat losses and design factors are considered. This ratio varies, depending on the combustion characteristics of the reservoir, from about 80 to 250 bbl water/MMscf of air injected. After the desired amount of reservoir has been heated, air injection can be stopped and continued water injection at accelerated rates floods the heated oil to ultimate recovery.

If the water-air injection ratio is further increased, the CTD process degenerates to partially quenched combustion, as shown by Fig. 172C. When the convection cooling velocity exceeds the burning front velocity, V_C controls frontal movements and the maximum temperature of the system approaches saturated steam temperature at the process pressure. The high-temperature zone is locally quenched, and the oxygen must move further downstream to react with residual oil at steam temperature,

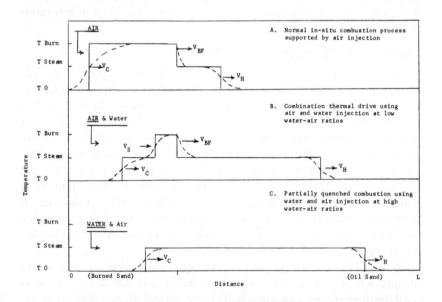

Fig. 172—*Combination Thermal Drive—The CTD process heats the oil sand to steam temperature by injecting water and air through the combustion zone.*

which is usually sufficiently high to cause rapid oxidation. Thus, only part of the available fuel is used.

Partially quenched combustion is frequently characterized by a decrease in carbon dioxide generation and an increase in oxygenated petroleum products. If the temperature in the heated zone is less than ignition temperature, the reaction mechanism can shift to where only low-temperature oxidation occurs, and if the oil is not susceptible to these reactions, no additional heat will be generated.

It is obvious that CTD can reduce the total air injected because most of the reservoir is heated only to saturated steam temperature, or less, rather than to the high temperatures illustrated by Fig. 172A. Producing wells can be operated at lower temperatures, and the injected water dilutes acidic formation fluids and minimizes their corrosive effect. Cost-saving features of CTD appear promising. The CTD process should be considered for application when the reservoir lithology is compatible with air-water injection. It is particularly attractive for reservoirs that are expected to yield high oil recoveries at steam temperatures, and its accelerated heat front advance increases the production rate of even highly viscous crude oils long before the high-temperature front reaches producing wells.

The combustion process has also been used to stimulate production wells on a cyclic basis, and the high-temperature process has been used to stimulate water injection wells in low-permeability formations.

Laboratory Evaluation of Combustion Drive

The combustion drive process has been shown to have certain basic similarities to other types of drive mechanisms. The unusual aspect of the combustion drive is the presence of the moving heat front. For maximum oil recovery by this means, the heat front should be carefully controlled both as to its rate and direction of movement. The role of laboratory work in evaluating the controlling variables cannot be over-emphasized. Just as laboratory tests on rock cores are useful in evaluating and studying primary and waterflood operations, laboratory combustion-tube studies provide information necessary for use in the design of a combustion drive project.

In these laboratory experiments, reservoir oil and water are mixed with sand in proportion to that found in the reservoir. It is desirable to use core material from the reservoir when possible and, in general, field conditions are simulated. One of the most important results obtained from a laboratory experiment is the amount of fuel deposited on the sand by the reservoir oil. The fuel deposited usually ranges from 1 to 2 lb/100 lb of sand. Factors that may effect the amount of fuel deposited on the sand by the crude oil are: the rate of front advance, the viscosity of the oil, oil composition, pressure gradient, composition of oxidizing gas and specific surface area of the formation rock. Generally, the heavy, viscous crude oils leave more fuel than do light, high-gravity crude oils.

Fuel consumption can be combined with the quantity of air injected to indicate the amount of air required to move the burning front through a unit of reservoir rock. The air required has been found to range from about 200 to 400 scf air/cu ft of oil sand burned clean. Air required depends primarily on the amount of fuel consumed, the type of oxidizing reaction and the efficiency of oxygen utilization at the combustion front. Based on field operations to date, it appears that an oxygen utilization efficiency of more than 90 per cent can be achieved during periods of active combustion.

The linear laboratory studies conducted in combustion tubes may be resolved into areal sweep configurations by the use of potentiometric model studies. For developed, five-spot pattern operations, the areal sweep of the burning front at breakthrough into production wells is about 62 per cent of the pattern area, assuming uniform permeability within the pattern and infinite mobility ratio. In addition to limitations on areal sweep, such factors as gravitational effects, quenching caused by heat losses to overlying and underlying strata, and incomplete ignition of the sand face at the injection well may limit the vertical sweep of the burning front. At present, however, no definite conclusion can be drawn from either laboratory or field information concerning the vertical sweep efficiency of the combustion process; as mentioned previously, however, thermal energy is transferred to the formation above, below and ahead of the burning front so that high oil recovery is achieved by the process.

Design and Control of a Combustion Drive

Air injection rate can be calculated from potentiometric model data once a reasonable schedule for the rate of burning front advance for a given pattern is established. To establish the rate of burning front advance, the minimum rate that will support combustion must be considered. Other pertinent factors are the sweep efficiency, air injectivity, the maximum allowable injection pressure and the rate at which the production wells can produce oil. A rate of burning front advance between 0.25 and 1 ft/D has been found desirable.

Once the air injection schedule is set, the gas and oil production systems and treating facilities can be designed. As the burning front moves through the formation, oil is displaced by a piston-like action. The theoretical oil-displacement rate varies directly with the velocity of the burning front, the vertical and areal sweep and the recoverable oil content of the formation. The actual production rates realized from the combustion drive could be expected to correspond closely to the theoretical displacement rate, but the production rate would also depend upon such factors as oil viscosity, sand thickness, effective permeability to oil and other factors that enter into conventional flow relations. Oil production rates associated with the combustion process are much higher than the primary production rate. This is especially true in fields containing high-viscosity oil where low primary rates are experienced. For example, in the South Belridge field, Calif., a recent combustion test increased production of the 13° API oil from 20 to 140 B/D.

Reported oil recoveries by in-situ combustion field tests have ranged from 51 to as high as 80 per cent of the oil in place at the start of the test. These high recoveries were realized in relatively short periods of time. In some fields the gravity of the produced oil was increased 1 or 2° API and the viscosity was reduced below that of the original reservoir oil.

Since the movement of the burning front depends directly upon the amount of air injected, the oil production rate is proportional to the air injection rate. Injected air-produced oil ratios (AOR) experienced in field tests have ranged from 10,000 to 30,000 cu ft/bbl. After the oil bank is formed, the AOR drops rapidly and it is frequently as low at 5,000 cu ft/bbl during periods of efficient operation.

Movement of the burning front is controlled by regulating the supply of air to the burning region. To realize maximum oil recovery from a combustion drive operation, however, the direction of movement of the heat front also must be controlled. Combustion gases produced from each section of the well are analyzed for carbon dioxide, carbon monoxide, oxygen, nitrogen and hydrocarbon content. The measurements of quantity and composition of the produced gas are then utilized to determine the amount of fuel consumed, which is related to the reservoir volume swept by the burning front, using other information gained from the combustion-tube studies. For a pilot-type operation, this information can be used to adjust production well pressures to control the burning front as desired. In this manner, symmetry is maintained insofar as is possible. Perhaps more precise control can be achieved in a developed field operation where several well patterns are conducted simultaneously. In this case, both the injection and production pressures between different well patterns could be varied to control and direct the burning front.

Reservoir Conditions Suitable for Combustion Drive

Reservoir conditions suitable for the combustion drive process have not been clearly and completely defined by field tests to date. The early development of the process has been limited to shallow depths for economic reasons. There are, however, certain reservoir characteristics found in shallow oil sands that make the thermal methods appear attractive. One characteristic is, of course, low reservoir temperature. Temperatures between 60 and 80°F usually exist in shallow oil sands. At these temperatures, even oils in the gravity range of 25 to 35° API will often be too viscous for efficient recovery by conventional primary or secondary methods. For the more viscous, heavier crude oils (10 to 20° API), thermal recovery methods are particularly suitable.

Shallow formations normally have low reservoir pressures so that air can be injected at a reasonable pressure. Consequently, air-compression costs for combustion operations are minimized. However, the effective permeability of the reservoir to air is a controlling parameter, and for low injection pressures to be realized, highly permeable formations are more desirable. Combustion has been initiated at depths greater than 7,000 ft.

Combustion has been maintained in formations varying from 5 to 50 ft and greater in thickness. Heat losses are greater in the thinner sand sections, and there is less oil in place per acre.

Thick sands, therefore, appear more suitable for oil recovery by in-situ combustion.

Many reservoir characteristics can be simulated in laboratory studies. Others cannot and must be investigated in the field. The effect of an adjacent gas or water zone must be carefully investigated to assure that air is injected into the oil sand through the burning front and not into an overlying or underlying strata. The shape and areal extent of the reservoir may govern the type of well pattern employed. In one field a five-spot pattern will be practical, but in another field a line drive may be best suited. Only after careful study can the most efficient method of field development be selected.

Exploitation of Petroleum Reservoirs For Maximum Profit

Production practices that provide maximum oil recovery are usually determined only after lengthy reservoir study, which is dependent for accuracy upon the completeness and reliability of the information available concerning the producing reservoir. Most reservoir problems deal with future operations in the light of past performance, and considerable data of all types are often necessary before a satisfactory solution may be made. Accurate and dependable basic data are, therefore, the corner-stones of any sound reservoir engineering study.

Reservoir Engineering Data

The engineer must utilize four broad types of data in conjunction with reservoir studies. These include (1) data concerning the reservoir rock, (2) properties of fluids in the rock, (3) a pressure history and (4) a production history of the reservoir. Reservoir rock and fluid data are usually obtained during the development of the reservoir, whereas pressure and production data are obtained over the entire period of operations.

Properties of Reservoir Rock

Required data concerning the reservoir rock include estimates of total rock pore volume in both oil and gas zones of the reservoir. These volumes are obtained by means of contour and isopach, or net pay thickness maps of the reservoir. Proper values for porosity and connate-water content applied to reservoir volume determine total volumes of hydrocarbons in place originally in the reservoir. It is necessary, therefore, to have the best available quantitative information on porosity, permeability (both absolute and relative) and connate water in the reservoir rock. In addition, it is desirable to have qualitative information on the character and homogeneity of the reservoir and the continuity between the reservoir and the adjacent water-bearing formation. Conventional and special core analyses, drill-stem testing and various types of logging provide the sources for these data.

Properties of Reservoir Fluids

Properties of the reservoir hydrocarbon fluids may be obtained from laboratory analysis of a subsurface or recombined oil and gas sample. The more important fluid properties obtained are: hydrocarbon analysis of reservoir fluids; flash gas liberation (including shrinkage factor), dissolved gas-oil ratio and oil gravity measurements; pressure-volume-temperature data; differential gas liberation data; differential oil-shrinkage data; and reservoir fluid viscosity data.

Production Data

Production history data include a tabulation of the periodic production of oil, gas and water from the reservoir. Total volumes of fluids produced from the reservoir are used for problems dealing with the reservoir as a whole, whereas well production data deal with individual wells. In addition, productive capacity, location on the structure and producing interval must be known for each well.

Pressure Data

Periodic reliable reservoir pressure measurements, or at least a reliable pressure trend, should be obtained. This pressure history should conform to the periodic production history. For problems dealing with reservoirs as a whole, average reservoir pressures are obtained based on all wells, or a number of key wells, while problems dealing with individual wells require per-well data.

Reservoir Behavior and Methods of Study

The second phase of a reservoir engineering study deals with mathematical interpretation of changes that take place with production and time. When a reservoir is discovered, fluids in the rock pores are usually under equilibrium conditions or at rest. This equilibrium is disturbed as oil is produced from the rock by the natural drive. Any reservoir found in nature may be producing under any one or a combination of the three basic reservoir drives. The purposes of a reservoir study are to determine the physical nature of the reservoir, the type and magnitude of the natural reservoir drive operating, the way the corresponding drive mechanism influences reservoir behavior and, finally, the means to control this behavior in a manner that will provide economic return to the operator.

Several basic tools have been developed to determine performance of the various types of reservoirs. These tools are mathematical, to be sure; just as the pipe wrench is the tool of the pipeliner, so is the mathematical equation a tool of the engineer.

Usually some 10 per cent or more of the recoverable oil must be produced from the reservoir before sufficient reservoir life has transpired to permit a reasonably accurate determination of reservoir behavior. Basically, a reservoir study involves application of some standardized set of mathematical relations—the terms made up from reservoir, fluid, pressure and production data, and the calculations made to determine past reservoir behavior. If calculated behavior agrees with observed past behavior, the mathematical interpretation of the reservoir is said to be valid and the set of equations is used to make predictions of future performance. If calculated and observed past behavior do not agree, the mathematical approach must be altered or data re-examined and correct data substituted to duplicate past performance. Then, and only then, can reasonably accurate predictions of future reservoir performance be made using the developed mathematical equations. Several types of machines have been developed to permit rapid mathematical calculations in reservoir studies. In many instances the machines permit calculations which would be too laborious and time-consuming to perform by hand calculators. These machines are electric analyzers, analog devices, digital computers and potentiometric models. Accuracy and applicability of machine results are limited by the accuracy of the data used and calculation method set up in the machine — just as with the hand calculator procedure.

The aspects of reservoir performance determined by mathematical calculations vary, of course, depending upon drive mechanism active in producing oil from the reservoir. Performance characteristics of the various drives were discussed in Chapter 5; however, the variations in approach to study of the various types of reservoirs are outlined in the following paragraphs.

Dissolved Gas Drive Reservoirs

Mathematical relations for analysis of the dissolved gas drive reservoir have been published by many authors and have been modified by various engineers, but the various procedures are essentially the same. These processes merely use some form of volumetric or material balance and may be either trial-and-error or direct calculations, depending upon the assumptions involved. The volumetric balance is a mathematical equation balancing volume of materials withdrawn from the reservoir with an equal volume taking their place. In this case, materials withdrawn are oil and gas and taking their place are expanded volumes of remaining oil and gas in the reservoir. The bulk of the expansion comes from gas liberated from the oil throughout the reservoir. Fig. 173 illustrates this basic relation. Attendant pressure is determined by expansibility of the remaining oil and gas, and the gas-oil ratio by relative permeability and fluid saturation relations of the porous rock.

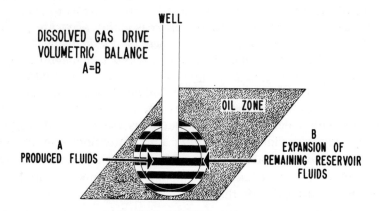

Fig. 173—*Dissolved gas drive reservoir illustrating volumetric balance method of calculating behavior. (Courtesy* WORLD OIL.—*May, 1951.)*

Water Drive Reservoirs

Two types of calculations are employed in the engineering study of water drive reservoirs—the study of volumetric behavior and the study of displacement efficiency. Volumetric behavior is determined by simultaneous solution of volumetric balance and some radial flow or unsteady-state water influx equation. The volumetric balance, in this case, balances produced oil, gas and water (as materials withdrawn) with expansion of the remaining reservoir oil and gas together with the water that entered the reservoir from the water basin (as the materials taking the place of the withdrawals). Fig. 174 illustrates this volumetric balance relation.

Fig. 175 illustrates location and direction of movement of water from which radial flow mechanics were conceived. The simultaneous calculation will determine the amount of water that has entered the reservoir and replaced oil. When this influx is satisfactorily determined by both equations for past behavior of the reservoir, the equations are considered applicable for use in predicting future reservoir behavior. Results of the volumetric behavoir computations involve fluid volumes; no geometry is

used. That is, these calculations do not tell the analyst where
the fluid movements are taking place. This information, needed
to answer operational questions, is obtained from displacement
studies.

Displacement efficiency calculations to determine recovery of
oil under various modes of operations can then be made. Fig. 176
illustrates schematically the mechanism of displacement of oil by
water encroachment. These calculations, of course, must be made
in conjunction with studies dealing with geometry, continuity and
degree of homogeneity of the particular reservoir.

The displacement calculations determine water saturation
and remaining oil saturation at different points in the reservoir
from the original oil-water contact after certain periods of time
as the water moves into the reservoir. With saturations thus
determined and amount of water that entered the reservoir determined by the volumetric balance and unsteady-state water
influx equations, the distance the oil-water contact has moved

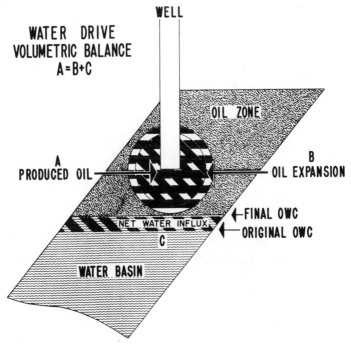

Fig. 174—*Water drive reservoir illustrating volumetric balance method of
calculating behavior. (Courtesy* WORLD OIL—*May, 1951.)*

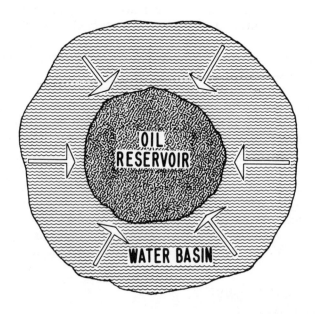

Fig. 175—*Radial flow of water into a reservoir in the unsteady-state "compressible fluids". (Courtesy* WORLD OIL—*May, 1951.)*

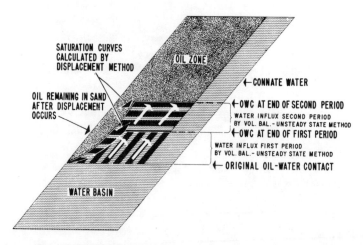

Fig. 176—*Displacement of oil by water illustrating method of calculating fraction of recovery. (Courtesy* WORLD OIL—*May, 1951.)*

up-structure is then determined on a volumetric basis. Schematic diagrams are used to obtain fluid inventories for each production period in the life of the reservoir. Fig. 176 represents an inventory of the reservoir fluids for the first two production periods. Of particular interest in this illustration is the quantity of oil remaining behind the displacing water. This volume is inversely related to the quantity of oil displaced by the water. By repeating displacement calculations with various assumed reservoir producing rates and water-oil ratios, operating conditions for optimum oil recovery can be determined.

Gas Cap Drive Reservoirs

Analysis of the gas cap drive reservoir also depends upon two types of calculations—volumetric behavior and displacement efficiency. The principal differences between analyzing the gas cap drive and the water drive reservoirs are that the volumetric balance is used solely to determine volumetric behavior (there being no water influx calculations in the gas cap drive reservoir), and the displacement calculations concern gas displacement of oil instead of water displacement of oil.

Volumetric behavior of the gas cap drive reservoir is analyzed with the same type volumetric balance equation used in water drive with modifications involving gas relative permeabilities to apply to gas cap drive reservoir conditions. Oil and gas from the oil zone and gas from the gas cap are treated by the volumetric balance as withdrawals, while oil and gas expansion in the oil zone together with gas-cap change are treated as materials replacing the withdrawals. Fig. 177 illustrates this volumetric balance relation. Again, as in the case of water drive reservoirs, volumetric behavior computations analyze volume changes. Further analysis is necessary, utilizing displacement calculations under different operations to determine changes in fluid distribution from which ultimate recovery from the reservoir under the different modes of operations can be predicted. Fig. 178 illustrates the mechanism of oil displacement by gas-cap expansion. The nature of gas displacement and appropriate calculations are similar to those dealing with water displacement. Again, as in the water drive reservoir, the quantity of oil remaining behind the displacing fluid (gas from the gas cap) is inversely related to amount of oil displaced by the gas.

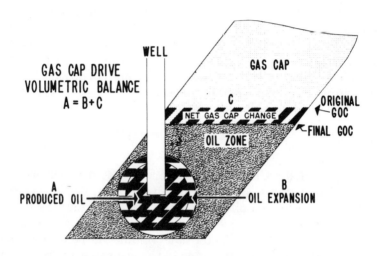

Fig. 177—*Gas cap drive reservoir illustrating volumetric balance method of calculating behavior. (Courtesy* WORLD OIL—*June, 1951.)*

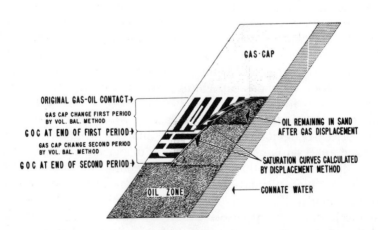

Fig. 178—*Displacement of oil by gas illustrating method of calculating fraction of recovery. (Courtesy* WORLD OIL—*June, 1951.)*

Combination Drive Reservoirs

A study of a combination drive reservoir presents more complications than other drives; however, there also are only two phases of this study—volumetric behavior and displacement efficiency computations. The volumetric behavior phase employs volumetric balance and unsteady-state radial flow equations to determine gas-cap change, water influx and pressure trends. The volumetric balance here balances produced oil, gas and water (as materials withdrawn) against oil and gas expansions in the oil zone together with gas-cap change and water influx into the reservoir (as materials taking the place of withdrawals). Fig. 179 illustrates this volumetric balance relation. Again these computations deal only with volumes; displacement studies and displacement efficiency calculations are used to obtain further infor-

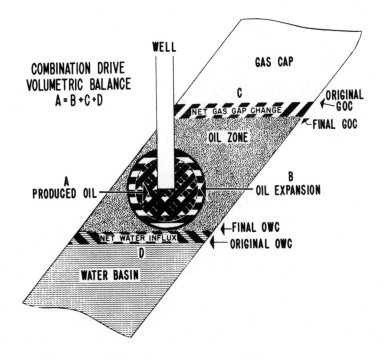

Fig. 179—*Combination drive reservoir illustrating volumetric balance method of calculating behavior. (Courtesy* WORLD OIL—*June, 1951.)*

mation regarding location and distribution of fluid saturations. In combination drive, however, displacement calculations involve volumes of both gas-cap encroachment and water influx into the reservoir.

Phase Behavior of Oil Reservoirs

Foregoing volumetric behavior and displacement efficiency discussions concern changes in volumes of fluid and their redistribution in the reservoir. Predicting these changes is of major importance, but it is only part of the problem. During the various phases of the hydrocarbon materials' journey from the pores to their ultimate goal in the consumers' market, they undergo substantial change. The reservoir fluid separates into two portions—liquid crude and natural gas. Different operating conditions at the separators produce different quantities of crude oil and gas from a given volume of oil in the ground. Behavior of the oil and gas as temperature and pressure conditions change is called phase behavior (Chapters 3 and 9). It is of major importance to control this behavior, both in the reservoir and at the surface, to obtain maximum recovery and production of the more valuable products. Mathematical relations have been derived and published whereby the phase behavior of reservoir oil and gas may be calculated. These are termed "flash" or "equilibrium" calculation.

Gas Reservoirs

Behavior of gas wells and reservoirs was discussed in Chapters 11 and 12. Of the various types of gas reservoirs, the condensate gas reservoir poses the greatest problems because both retrograde condensation of liquid in the reservoir and optimum separation of condensate from gas at the surface must be considered.

Phase behavior relationships, supported by proper laboratory data, are employed to determine quantities of condensable hydrocarbons present at various pressure and temperature conditions. These relationships are used to study hydrocarbon behavior in the reservoir to determine the amounts of liquid and gas recoverable under various modes of operation. The condensate reservoir may be produced by straight production, with or without a gasoline plant, or by cycling at either high or low reservoir pressures. Under any of these various methods, the presence and magnitude of a water drive must be considered to obtain reliable comparisons.

Verification and Interpretation of Reservoir Analyses

Perhaps the most important phase of any reservoir analysis is its verification by the analyst. The analyst must satisfy himself, as well as others, that his work properly reflects actual changes in fluid volumes in the reservoir. This is particularly true because operating program changes frequently involve large capital investments with negligible salvage values. Thus, an erroneous analysis could result in a large capital loss even though misinterpretation of actual reservoir behavior was recognized only a few years after completing the initial analysis. In addition, recommendations based on a non-representative analysis could result in adopting an operating program which would reduce rather than improve reservoir behavior efficiency. In essence, therefore, the analyst must know the limitations and uncertainties in the complete study. He must, insofar as possible, not only determine the effect of these limitations on final results, but also establish a reliable evaluation of the reservoir by comparing analysis results with available physical information.

Both regional and local comparisons can be made to establish reliability of the reservoir analysis. Regional comparisons merely determine if the reservoir performs in accord with others in the general area and with general geological features existing in the adjacent area. Local comparisons concern individual well performance and involve such things as checking movements of the gas cap and water zone to verify calculated gas-cap expansion or shrinkage and water influx.

Because it is his job to determine reservoir performance, recovery and behavior under various operating plans designed to augment that recovery, the petroleum engineer must also reduce his analysis to a series of operational recommendations to present to management. This phase of reservoir engineering is the interpretation of the analysis and covers many major considerations:

1. Determining the maximum efficient rate of production.
2. Evaluating the economic payout of such operations as pressure maintenance by water or gas and of secondary recovery programs.
3. Evaluating the economics of imposing controls on production to obtain maximum recovery.
4. Planning and evaluating workover programs.
5. Planning and evaluating artificial lift programs.

Note that economics play a great part in final recommendations. Unlike some other business enterprises, the petroleum industry is concerned with depletable natural resources (oil and gas reservoirs), which are both difficult and expensive to find and develop. The reservoir engineer must therefore investigate, along with reservoir performance and means for improving that performance, such economic considerations as capital investments, ultimate profits, the period required to return the money, rate of income, etc. Economic analysis is as much a part of the reservoir study as performance calculations. It merits the same careful work as all other phases of the study and is the particular phase of the study upon which management bases a course of action.

The reservoir analyst must also keep abreast of the legal aspects of controlling production operations—either primary, auxiliary or secondary recovery. He must understand the laws and regulations governing production of our natural resources and the industry. Knowing these legal limitations will prevent wasting time on operations which may not be given favor by regulatory bodies and courts.

The Exploitation Team

Development and delineation of the reservoirs are best accomplished by applying a combination of geologic and engineering principles, each complementing the other. When the two complementary sciences are integrated, reservoir development is generally more efficient. It results in properly located and completed wells, minimum costs for drilling and completion, minimum wells drilled and maximum efficiency of oil recovery through good reservoir drainage pattern. Proper integration of geological and engineering effort is as important as combining reservoir engineering and field production practices.

In the discovery well, the completion interval is determined almost entirely upon a geologic basis—upon a detailed lithologic study of the producing section utilizing cores, logs and tests. In subsequent wells, however, selecting a completion interval and formation treatment can best be accomplished through joint consideration by geologist and engineer. In this manner, both geologic information (such as fluid contacts) and engineering information (such as type of producing drive) can guide completion practices. Thus, a carefully planned development program involves well completions and well spacing based upon complete geologic and engineering interpretations of all available data. Such a planned approach can minimize initial capital outlay for development and future expenditures for well workovers or recompletions to achieve the most efficient reservoir operations.

Drilling excess wells can be prevented during reservoir development by engineering determinations of reserves to be drained by each well. Such reserve estimates utilize both geological and engineering data, with certain of the geological data being interpreted by engineering methods and certain of the engineering data being interpreted by geological methods.

Planning production operations to recover the most oil from the reservoir primarily concerns the reservoir engineer. Production is concerned with economics as well as over-all recovery of hydrocarbons, yet both are intimately associated. Increased production rates raise income while, in many cases, adjusted production rates increase recovery. Therefore, obtaining maximum economic recovery—the crux of the production problem—can be achieved with an optimum balance between conservation, economics and operations.

With management's guidance, the reservoir engineer and geologist must work together as an oil exploitation team to attain the best results. Their united effort can provide management with the reliable up-to-date engineering studies and reservoir data often needed quickly for making important decisions. During drilling operations, a carefully planned "key-well program" of coring, logging and testing can (1) provide necessary data during development pertaining to the reservoir drive mechanism, (2) indicate a more effective well location or spacing arrangement, (3) help recognize additional potential reserves and (4) provide data needed later for pressure maintenance or secondary exploitation.

Reservoir engineering today is helping the industry realize more efficient and complete oil recoveries than ever before. New recovery processes of unprecedented efficiency, including miscible and thermal drives, will improve chances for achieving even higher oil recoveries in the future. To attain maximum over-all profit, however, the industry must fully recognize the role of reservoir technology and its fundamental concern with maximum economic recovery, consequently integrating it completely into the business of petroleum reservoir exploitation.